Petrographic
Modal
Analysis _____

Petrographic Modal Analysis

An elementary statistical appraisal

FELIX CHAYES
Geophysical Laboratory
Carnegie Institution of Washington

New York · John Wiley & Sons, Inc.

London · Chapman & Hall, Limited

". . . the mountains *must indeed be examined with the microscope.*"

H. C. Sorby, 1856

Preface

The sound development of petrology, whether naturalistic or experimental, demands considerable information about the quantitative modal composition of rocks. In certain areas of petrographic inquiry, further development—indeed, even the resolution of longstanding controversies—seems almost impossible without an abundance of this kind of information. The amount and caliber of it available to us will also powerfully influence the rate of development in many other areas.

Despite increased interest and activity in the field of modal analysis the subject is ignored in nearly all textbooks on petrology and barely mentioned in most on petrography. The student is obliged to acquire the necessary background from scattered journal articles of uneven quality, mostly rather specialized, and often flatly inconsistent or contradictory. There is no single work to which the advanced undergraduate or beginning graduate—or anyone else, for that matter—may turn for an account sufficiently complete to enable him to decide whether and how he ought to set about using the technique in his own researches.

What the student needs, and what I have attempted to give him, are: (a) a clear description of the geometrical basis of the method; (b) a review and summary of techniques and instrumentation; (c) a careful discussion of reproducibility; (d) a definition and numerical characterization of analytical error; (e) a sense of the importance of analytical error in the design and planning of sampling experiments.

The subject has now advanced to the stage at which a condensed general treatment of the first three of these is possible; such a treatment is attempted in chapters 1–6, inclusive. One can always define analytical error generally, but it is only in some particular situa-

vii

tion that one may put numerical flesh on the bones of the definition. The same difficulty arises in the discussion of the effect of analytical error on experimental design. The experimentalist senses and the mathematician symbolizes the relationship in an a priori way, but specific numerical recommendations can only be developed in a practical situation.

Beginning with chapter 7, and continuing through chapter 10, therefore, the discussion is necessarily confined to a particular rock type, the only one, so far as I know, on which a study of this sort has been conducted. Most of the work presented in these chapters has not appeared before. It is included in the hope that it will serve as a model—albeit one which will certainly require extensive revision —for those who may be interested in developing for other rocks the type of information now rapidly accumulating for the two-feldspar granites. Ultimately something of the sort will probably have to be done for every major rock type. I hope my errors of design and judgment are sufficiently penetrating that others may profit by them.

Chapter 2 is included primarily as an antidote to the habitual and largely uncritical skepticism about the potentialities of modal analysis in the study of sediments and the finer-grained metamorphic rocks. Readers who do not share this skepticism or have no immediate concern with laminated rocks will find that the argument of chapter 2 is not essential to an appreciation of the work of succeeding chapters. Chapter 11, on the other hand, is designed as a warning to those who may be tempted to apply modal analysis to rocks to which it should not be applied.

I should caution the reader that this book is not intended as a literature review. No paper is mentioned merely for the sake of completeness, and except in chapter 3 no particular attention is paid to priority. Indeed, the development of the subject has been so unsystematic that this is scarcely possible. If a recent paper states a problem more clearly or solves it more satisfactorily than an older one, the recent one is given preference in the discussion, and in several cases the older one is not even mentioned. Readers interested in piecing together a history of the subject can get off to a good start with the excellent bibliography given by Larsen and Miller.

It will be obvious even to the casual reader that this book is something of a hybrid. Resting heavily on elementary statistical argument, it is not a book about statistics. Anyone who has participated in the development of modal analysis realizes that a sharp subdivision of the subject into statistical and non-statistical categories is no longer either possible or desirable. This raises the puzzling question of how results reached by statistical methods should be presented to an audience most of whom, even now, have had no training in the subject.

Fortunately, the argument is for the most part both simple and straightforward. I have tried to write so that geologists completely unfamiliar with statistics (and even those who, whether from choice or necessity, plan to continue in this blissful condition) may nevertheless follow its general outline and make use of its major results. It will take a bit of doing, but I believe it can be done. Most of the commoner terms and phrases that have received special definition in elementary statistics retain enough of their general import so that, with some allowance for lack of rigor, they still convey much the same thing to the non-statistical reader as to the reader with some training in the subject. Technical jargon has been avoided—evaded would perhaps be a better term—whenever this could be managed without undue expansion of the text, but has been used freely, and without extended explanation, whenever necessary. Similarly, numerical results are used liberally, but calculation procedures are described only when they are extremely simple or of a type not likely to be discussed in an elementary statistics textbook.

Instead of attempting the usual statistical explanation or laboring the book with footnotes, I have inserted an appendix containing a somewhat annotated statistical bibliography. Readers unfamiliar with the subject will find here references in which the various statistical terms and procedures employed are described in a fashion I could not hope to equal.

The book grows out of a series of lectures delivered to a graduate seminar in petrology at the California Institute of Technology during the winter of 1955. I am grateful to the staff and members of the Division of Geological Sciences for gracious hospitality and stimulating criticism. I am also indebted to several colleagues at the Geophysical Laboratory and to Earl Ingerson and J. D. H. Donnay for careful criticism of parts of the manuscript. The discussion of oriented rocks contained in the original lecture notes was so unsatisfactory that I planned to omit the subject from the published version; what now appears as chapter 2 was written largely because of the insistent encouragement of W. S. MacKenzie. Some of the experimental data used in chapter 8 were described briefly in *Year Book* No. 53 of the Carnegie Institution of Washington, and much of the material in chapters 1, 4, and 5 is reprinted here by permission of the editors of the *American Mineralogist* and the *Journal of Geology*. The substance of chapter 11 appeared originally in the *Mineralogical Magazine*

and is reprinted here by permission of the councilors of the Mineralogical Society of London.   Finally, it is pleasant to record my gratitude
to the staff of the Statistical Engineering Laboratory of the National
Bureau of Standards, and particularly to J. M. Cameron, for advice,
assistance, and encouragement extending over several years.

FELIX CHAYES

Washington, D. C.
July, 1956

Contents

Introduction

This book is intended for petrographers but may also be read by practical statisticians who have no knowledge of petrography. Modal analysis is still so sparingly used in geology that many readers of both types may appreciate a brief statement of the character and purpose of the procedure.

A rock is a mineral aggregate. To the petrologist, the kinds and amounts of mineral species it contains are matters of first importance. With regard to determination of the *kinds* of minerals present, petrography is a highly developed descriptive science, and we shall not be further concerned here with the general problem of qualitative identification.

The composition of rock expressed in terms of the relative *amounts* of minerals actually present is called a *mode*. We refer to a procedure which yields such a statement, and usually to the statement itself, as a *modal analysis*. Modes may be obtained by recalculation from bulk chemical analysis, by the counting of crushed fragments, or by the measurement of relative areas underlain by each of the mineral species in a polished slab or thin section of the rock.

The compositions of the constituent minerals are rarely well enough known so that much reliance can be placed on modes recalculated from bulk analyses. Although the procedure of counting sized, crushed fragments seems quite straightforward, the results are of questionable value because of sampling difficulties which have not yet been carefully evaluated. At present very few modes are determined by fragment counting.

Modes were determined by areal measurements on polished slabs before the development of the thin section—or, at any rate, before the thin section became a common adjunct of petrography—and this is still the preferred procedure in rather special circumstances. Discrimination between some of the rock-forming minerals is difficult or impossible under reflected light, however, and the number of reliable modes obtained by measurements made on polished slabs is almost vanishingly small.

1

Thus, although any procedure which estimates the actual mineral composition of a rock is, strictly speaking, a modal analysis, nearly all modes are estimated by areal measurement performed on thin sections under the microscope. The instruments used for this purpose are now fairly numerous and quite varied in design and construction. Their proper application always has the same goal, viz., a reliable estimate of the relative proportions of the measurement area underlain by minerals of different species, and they all secure this information in one of two ways. Either they cumulate intercept lengths along a set of parallel equidistant lines, or they tally the frequencies with which the members of a symmetrical point grid are underlain by minerals of each species.

The equivalence of areal proportions to volumetric proportions was suspected and announced by Delesse in 1848. (It may have been known before this in other sciences, but there is no earlier mention of it in the literature of geology.) Though Delesse used the relation to good advantage, he did not actually prove it. Nor did any other geologist. As a consequence it was always regarded with considerable skepticism. Those who placed any confidence in it might justify their credulity by pointing to an experiment, commonly too small to demonstrate anything at all, in which the bulk chemical composition calculated from the mean of a few modes of dubious quality agreed fairly well with an actual chemical analysis of unknown quality. Sometimes the procedure was reversed, and measured modes were compared with modes calculated from chemical analyses. Occasional tests of this kind could convince only those who had a powerful will to believe. And geology is by tradition an agnostic science.

The development of the subject was correspondingly slow. Indeed, what little there was of it was primarily concerned with instrumentation. In the century following Delesse's announcement of the method it is difficult to cite a single geological research in which critical issues were either illuminated or decided by means of modal analyses. Even the currently increasing popularity of quantitative minerological rock classifications, in which the very basis of classification is modal composition, has so far proved insufficient to stimulate activity in this field.

The principal problems of modal analysis are: (a) the equivalence of areal and volumetric proportions, (b) the reproducibility of estimates of areal proportions, and (c) the sampling efficiency of thin sections. These are all problems which are readily susceptible of statistical examination and difficult though perhaps not impossible to study satisfactorily in any other way. During the first century of its career modal analysis enjoyed a kind of extra-statistical existence during which it promised much and accomplished practically nothing. Since 1945 it has been subjected to a persistent though rather elementary statistical reorientation and has already begun to stand on its own feet as an independent discipline; if the trend continues we may reasonably expect that it will soon assume its rightful place as the simplest, quickest, and cheapest analytical procedure available to the petrologist. The immediate future holds the promise of a development of quantitative petrography as brilliant and as productive as the great flowering of qualitative petrography at the close of the last century.

1

The geometrical basis
of modal analysis _____

The lack of a satisfactory and easily comprehended analytical demonstration of the validity of thin-section analysis has probably been the most important deterrent to the development of the subject.   Both Delesse and Rosiwal, by whom the technique was first proposed, were aware of the weakness of their analytical arguments.   Despite occasional attempts since their day, no satisfactory solution of the general problem is available in the geological literature.

Delesse's original announcement of the method attracted little attention. His procedure was hopelessly time-consuming, yet a half century elapsed before anyone attempted to improve upon it.   Rosiwal's improvement reduced the time per analysis to something on the order of many hours for a medium- or fine-grained rock.   And the next—really the first—substantial improvement, the Shand recording micrometer, was not announced until 1916, sixty-eight years after Delesse and eighteen after Rosiwal.

The period between the announcement of the Delesse method and the appearance of the Shand micrometer is precisely the golden age of descriptive petrography.   The petrographers of that day could have made excellent use of reliable quantitative modes, and many of them were keenly aware of the need for such information.   They could have had it— and the petrography of our day would have profited immeasurably thereby—with instrumentation far simpler than was then developing in the sister science of optical crystallography.   But the appropriate instrumentation was not forthcoming.

Considering all the circumstances, it is reasonable to suppose that the root of the failure lay in the fact that no one, not even Delesse and certainly not Rosiwal, was really convinced of the validity of the geometrical theory. In the language of today, the petrographers who should have taken prompt and thorough advantage of the Delesse method seem always to have been

4

bothered by the fear that their results would be inconsistent, that differences between analysis would contain large, unknown, and essentially unknowable, contributions which had nothing to do with the real differences between rocks.

This may be reading too much into a long record of indifference and inertia. It cannot be denied, however, that in the last quarter of the nineteenth century the time was ripe for full exploitation of quantitative modal analysis by descriptive petrography, that the method was available, that the necessary instrumentation was within easy reach, and that nothing happened. It is also true that the textbook and lecture material to which the average geology student is exposed today still contains far more of admonition and qualification than of endorsement and encouragement. Since most geologists have actually done very little modal analysis, this attitude can hardly stem from extensive practical experience. Rather, it is a kind of professional memory, an inheritance of the fear that except on very special rocks—and perhaps even on such rocks—the thing really doesn't work. Our first business is to dispel this fear. The question of whether modal analysis is *theoretically* sound has nothing to do with petrography. It is entirely a matter of geometrical probability. In this and the succeeding chapter the discussion will accordingly be much more of geometry than geology.

1. Point Sums as Estimators of Relative Areas

In Fig. 1 a small irregular area (B) is enclosed in a large irregular area $(B + W)$. The probability that a point located simply at random in $(B + W)^1$ will also lie in B is, by definition,

$$p = \left(\frac{A_B}{A_{(B+W)}}\right)$$

the ratio of the two areas.

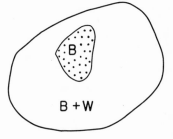

Fig. 1. Small area (B) enclosed in large area $(B + W)$, the ratio of the areas to be estimated by the sums of points chosen simply at random in the region $(B + W)$.

B

B + W

[1] I.e., in such fashion that each point in the area $(B + W)$ has the same probability of being selected as any other point.

The expected value of the number of points, $S(X)$, which fall in B in a particular sample containing n points, is

$$E(S(X_b)) = np = n \left(\frac{A_B}{A_{(B+W)}} \right) \tag{1.1}$$

As a proportion, μ, of the total count, this is

$$\mu = \frac{1}{n} E(S(X_b)) = p = \frac{A_B}{A_{(B+W)}} \tag{1.2}$$

Since its expected value is the ratio of the smaller to the larger area, the proportion of the total count that falls in the smaller area is an unbiased estimate of that ratio. (In the language of thin-section analysis, $A_{(B+W)}$ is the total measurement area available in any thin section, and p is the proportion of that area occupied by mineral B, whether as a single large grain or many small ones.)

2. PARALLEL LINES AS ESTIMATORS OF RELATIVE AREAS

The areas under the curves in Fig. 2 are obviously

$$A_1 = \int_a^d y_1 \, dx, \qquad A_2 = \int_b^c y_2 \, dx$$

Let us suppose that ordinates are to be erected at points along OX chosen simply at random in the region $a < x < d$. The element of frequency is thus dx, and the total frequency is

$$F = \frac{1}{d-a} \int_a^d dx = 1 \tag{1.3}$$

The expected value of y_1 is then

$$E(y_1) = \frac{1}{d-a} \int_a^d y_1 \, dx = \frac{A_1}{d-a} \tag{1.4}$$

and for y_2

$$E(y_2) = \frac{1}{d-a} \int_b^c y_2 \, dx = \frac{A_2}{d-a} \tag{1.5}$$

(In the regions $x < b$ and $x > c$, $g(x)$ is undefined and y_2 is zero.)

The ratio of the average ordinates is thus a consistent estimate of the ratio of the areas, for it is an estimate of the parent value μ_2/μ_1, and

$$\frac{\mu_2}{\mu_1} = \frac{E(y_2)}{E(y_1)} = \frac{A_2}{(d-a)} \cdot \frac{(d-a)}{A_1} = \frac{A_2}{A_1} \tag{1.6}$$

Now the expected value of the sum of the ordinate lengths under either curve is

$$E[\textstyle\sum(Y_i)] = N\mu_i = NE(y_i) \tag{1.7}$$

where N is the total number of traverses made in a particular random

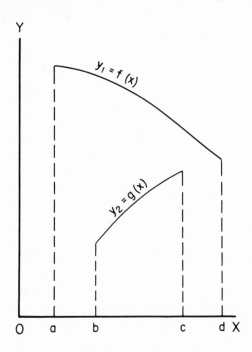

Fig. 2. Open areas under two curves, the ratio of the areas to be estimated by sums of ordinates chosen simply at random in the region $a < x < d$.

sampling of the region $a < x < b$. Again the *ratio of the sums of ordinates is a consistent estimate of the ratio of the areas, for*

$$\frac{E[\textstyle\sum(Y_2)]}{E[\textstyle\sum(Y_1)]} = \frac{N\mu_2}{N\mu_1} = \frac{A_2}{A_1} \tag{1.8}[2]$$

If in Fig. 2 the axes of reference are rotated about O, the area between the curves and OX will of course change, and so will the ratio of these areas. Thus, although $\dfrac{\sum(Y_2)}{\sum(Y_1)}$ is a consistent estimate for any particular orientation, its value will change with any change in the orientation of the axes.

[2] Equations (1.6) and (1.8) do not quite establish consistence. For this it is necessary that the variances of y_1 and y_2 be finite, but this is obviously the case since each varies over a finite range. See section 3 below.

Since the areas in Fig. 2 *do* change with rotation of the axes, any reliable estimate of areal ratios is also bound to change. If the areas in question are insensitive to location or rotation of the reference axes, however, eqs. (1.4–1.8) apply *regardless* of the position or orientation of the reference axes. Each of the closed curves in Fig. 3 may be divided into two parts by lines tangent to it and parallel to any chosen ordinate axis. In Fig. 3,

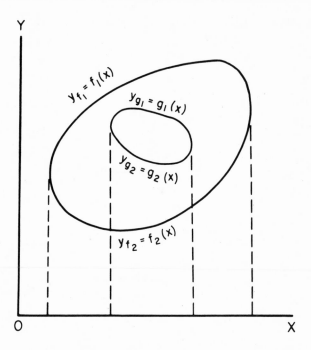

Fig. 3. Areas enclosed by two curves, the ratio of the areas to be estimated by sums of ordinates chosen simply at random in the region between the ordinates tangent to the larger area.

OY is used, and the tangents divide each curve into segments, $f_1(x)$, $f_2(x)$, and $g_1(x)$, $g_2(x)$, under each of which we can find $E(y)$ by means of eq. (1.4) or (1.5). The expected value of a difference is equal to the difference of the expected values of which it is formed, so we have at once that

$$E(y_{f_1} - y_{f_2}) = E(y_{f_1}) - E(y_{f_2}) = \frac{A_1}{d - a}$$

where A_1 is the area enclosed by the outer curve. Similarly,

$$E(y_{g_1} - y_{g_2}) = \frac{A_2}{d - a}$$

where A_2 is the area enclosed by the inner curve. The ratio we seek is

$$\frac{E(y_{g_1} - y_{g_2})}{E(y_{f_1} - y_{f_2})} = \frac{A_2}{A_1}$$

and this, being a function only of the enclosed areas, is obviously insensitive to the choice of axis.

In the language of thin-section analysis, OY is the traverse path or direction, OX is the traverse normal, and the unchanging areas are, respectively, the total area of measurement and the portion of it occupied by a particular mineral.

3. BIAS AND CONSISTENCE

In accordance with our announced intention of relying on the popular connotations of statistical terms whenever possible, we have so far neither defined nor distinguished between consistence and bias. The reader will have noted that estimates based on parallel lines were characterized as consistent whereas those based on points were called unbiased.

The sample average $\bar{x}$ is said to be a *consistent estimator* of the true, or population, mean μ if

$$Pr\{| \mu - \bar{x} | > \xi\} < \eta \quad \text{as} \quad n \to \infty$$

however small ξ and η.

The sample average $\bar{x}$ is said to be an *unbiased estimator* of μ, on the other hand, if the expected or most probable value of $\bar{x}$ is μ for *any $n \geqslant$* 1.

Lack of bias is obviously the more desirable property. Estimates of areal ratios based on the counting of randomly located points are both consistent and unbiased. Those based on parallel continuous lines are consistent but may be biased. The effect is easily shown by an example. Figure 4 shows a square inscribed in a right isosceles triangle; the area of the triangle is twice that of the square. Proceeding as before, we measure intercepts in each figure along randomly chosen lines parallel to the altitude of the triangle. By using eqs. (1.3–1.6) the student should be able to show that

$$\frac{E(y_2)}{E(y_1)} = 0.5 = \frac{A_s}{A_T} \tag{1.9}$$

where A_s is the area of the square and A_T that of the triangle. From the point of view of modal analysis, this is, of course, the correct answer. The summation extends over all ordinates for each intercept and is completed before the ratio is calculated. Equation (1.9) suggests that the ratio of observed average (or total) intercept distances is a consistent estimator of A_s/A_T but, since it does not describe the situation for any

$n < \infty$, cannot of itself establish consistence. For this we have to rely on the central-limits theorem. The range, and hence the variance, σ^2, of each expected value is finite. From this it follows that with increase in n the distributions of the observed means of the numerator and denominator of eq. (1.9) approach normality with variances σ_1^2/n, σ_2^2/n. And from this, finally, it follows that for n sufficiently large the inequality used as the definition of consistence does in fact hold.

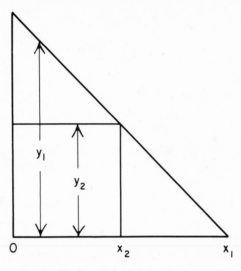

Fig. 4. Square inscribed in isosceles triangle, the expected value of the ratio y_2/y_1 and the ratio (expected value of y_2)/(expected value of y_1) to be estimated from ordinates chosen simply at random in the region $0 < x < x_1$.

Suppose, however, that, instead of summing y_2 and y_1 separately before finding the ratio, we calculated the ratio at each ordinate. If $R_1 = y_2/y_1$, then, by construction

$$R_1 = \begin{cases} \dfrac{1}{2-x} & 0 < x \leqslant 1 \\[2mm] 0 & 1 < x \leqslant 2 \end{cases}$$

Following the same reasoning as before, we have that

$$E(R_1) = \frac{1}{2} \int_0^1 \frac{dx}{(2-x)} = 0.347 \qquad (1.10)$$

Thus, although A_s/A_T is the ratio of the expected values of the ordinates, it is clearly *not* the expected value of the ratio of ordinates.

Generalizing the terminology, we may say that the result of every modal analysis made with parallel lines, continuous or broken, is a value of the ratio R_n, where n denotes the number of terms summed (in numerator and denominator) before the ratio is calculated. Equation (1.9) shows that for n infinite the expected value of R_n is A_s/A_T, and the accompanying argument shows that R_n is a consistent estimator of A_s/A_T. Equation (1.10) shows that, despite its consistence, R_n is nevertheless a biased estimator of A_s/A_T. It follows that the bias must decrease with increase in n, but an a priori statement of the relation between bias and sample size is difficult even for such a simple figure as this. Fortunately, a good working approximation of it can be obtained easily by random sampling experiments. A suite of these gives the following result:

n	Number of Samples	Observed Mean	Theoretical Mean
1	100	0.3561	0.3466
2	100	0.4621	
5	100	0.4928	
20	25	0.5069	
100	1	0.4973	
∞			0.5000

The bias in general must decrease with increase in n, though, of course, the *rate* at which it falls off will differ from figure to figure. Theoretically, areal estimates based on parallel lines are nearly always subject to some bias. In the normal course of modal analysis, however, rather large numbers of traverses, on the order of 20 to 30, are summed before the final ratio is calculated. The "areas" involved are usually composed of discontinuous patches of complex outline. Under these circumstances, it is reasonable to argue that the bias is ordinarily much smaller than the random error of the process and is therefore of little or no practical importance.

4. THE PRACTICAL SITUATION IN MODAL ANALYSIS

Although it is easy to think about simple random samples, it is often difficult to collect them. In practice modal analyses are nearly always based on *systematic* rather than random sampling. With the continuous line integrators, we run parallel traverses at equal intervals. With the point counter we select points at the intersections of a symmetrical grid over the surface of the thin section. In the first case the location of the first traverse on the traverse normal fixes the location of all succeeding traverses. In the second, the selection of the first point fixes the location of all others.

A systematic sampling will usually be more precise than a simple random one. In Fig. 2, for instance, it is possible that none of the traverses in a particular, simple random sample happen to lie in the region $c \leqslant x \leqslant d$, and the result will almost certainly be a drastic overestimate of A_2/A_1. With systematic sampling, however, this cannot happen unless the traverse interval (k) is larger than $(d-c)$, and it may not happen even then. If $k < (d-c)$, the expected number of traverses in the region $c \leqslant x \leqslant d$ is $(d-c)/k$. For the same number of traverses, systematic sampling assures a much more even distribution of information over the measurement area.

Similarly, in Fig. 1, a simple random sampling might yield no points at all in A_B, or an excessive number might fall there, and in either case the estimated areal ratio would contain a large error. The frequency of drastic misestimates of this sort is much reduced by the use of a systematic sampling grid, even if the translation distances of the grid are large in relation to the projections of B on the grid axes. They are extremely unlikely if the grid translations are less than the projected lengths of B.

Although results based on systematic sampling are likely to be somewhat more precise than those based on simple random sampling, it can happen that the two procedures do not estimate the same mean. Current work (see Cochran, 1953) suggests that, on the whole, biases introduced by systematization will be trifling except in the event of linear or periodic trends. We shall have to return to this problem in connection with the analysis of oriented rocks. Here it is only necessary to point out that the difficulty arises not from any breakdown in the fundamental relation between lines (or points) and areas but *merely from the way in which we select the lines (or points)*. As we shall see, a remedy is available.

5. THE AREA-VOLUME OR DELESSE RELATION

The area-volume relation, which determines whether our estimates of relative area may also be regarded as consistent estimates of relative volume, is both simpler and more widely misunderstood than any other part of the theory of modal analysis.

If the area of a section of a solid parallel to the xy plane is a function of z, $A = f(z)$, and sections through the solid can be chosen—or can legitimately be thought of as chosen—simply at random normal to OZ in the region $c \leqslant z \leqslant d$, the element of frequency is dz, the total frequency is

$$F = \frac{1}{d-c} \int_c^d dz = 1$$

and the expected value of A is

$$E(A) = \frac{1}{d-c} \int_c^d A\,dz = \frac{V}{d-c} \tag{1.11}$$

where A and V represent area and volume respectively. We have at once that

$$\frac{E(A_a)}{E(A_t)} = \frac{V_a}{V_t} \tag{1.12}$$

where V_t is the total volume concerned and V_a is the part of it occupied by mineral A. *Thus, the ratio of the area occupied by mineral A to the area occupied by all minerals (the total measurement area) is a consistent estimate of the volume percentage of mineral A in the rock.* This we shall call the Delesse relation. Considering the history of the subject we may pause long enough to stress:

1. that it says nothing whatever about the way in which the estimates of relative areas are to be obtained;

2. that it says nothing whatever about the shapes or orientations of the mineral grains.

Most "explanations" of the Delesse relation attempt to struggle through without a formulation of this type, and since this is impossible they end up as bowdlerizations in which the relation is pictured as holding "approximately," "under certain conditions," or, sometimes, not at all (see for instance an astonishing article by A. A. Julien). Where the general nature of the relation is apprehended, the explanations stumble over attempts to present a "realistic" interpretation of eq. (1.11) or its analogue, with dz pressed into service as the thickness of the thin section or $(d - c)$ as either the section or the specimen thickness. These errors are worth separate discussion.

In the first place, if dz is regarded as a finite quantity, however small, eq. (1.11) is literally nonsense; in conjunction with the integral sign it is an announcement that we are going to operate with A according to certain rules. Assigning a finite value to dz is a direct violation of the first and most important of these rules. Anyone who wishes to do so may cite Rosiwal (1898, p. 163) as a precedent, but this does not materially alter the situation. In the usual experimental situation a thin-section analysis is an analysis of an *area*.

Whereas no numerical value whatever may be assigned to dz without invalidating eq. (1.11), the equation remains valid for any of a wide range of values of $(d - c)$. As long as the section may be regarded as drawn simply at random normal to OZ in the interval $(d - c)$, the numerical value of $(d - c)$ is of no consequence. The random selection of a thin section is a consistent sampling of some volume. Whether the volume in question is of the order of a hand specimen, an outcrop, a pluton, or a batholith is determined by sampling of a different kind and order than we have been discussing.

The only measurements made in a thin-section analysis are estimates of the numerator and denominator on the left side of eq. (1.12); passage from the left side of the equation to the right does not require that we either know or assign a numerical value to $(d - c)$ and becomes impossible if we attempt to assign such a value to dz.

The possibility of bias is more bothersome in connection with the Delesse relation than in the measurement of areas, since the volume in whose composition we are immediately interested is usually a hand specimen and we want to use as few thin sections per hand specimen as possible. On fine-grained specimens, in fact, we ordinarily stop with a single thin section. Without making restrictive assumptions about the spatial distribution of minerals through the specimen we cannot exclude the possibility that a single section may be a biased sample. Except as they deal with gross and readily observable characteristics—banding, foliation, and the like—such assumptions usually pre-suppose a knowledge of rocks which we simply do not have.

It is true, of course, that, in the absence of banding, foliation, lineation, etc., there is ordinarily no reason to suppose that inhomogeneities of a type likely to introduce bias exist, and we may thus make a reasonably safe guess that there will usually be no bias, e.g., that a randomly chosen area will provide an unbiased sample of a volume of any shape in much the way that a randomly chosen point samples an area of any shape. It would be much more satisfactory to be able to announce simply that bias is in fact absent unless circumstances favoring it are clearly evident. Unfortunately, this is not now possible.

A rather curious escape from the dilemma has been suggested by Bankier, who was the first to note the confusion of bias and consistence in the work of the writer. Bankier points out that the line-area bias described in section 3 above disappears if the denominator of the ratio is constant. The denominator is simply the length of an individual traverse, and if this is the same from traverse to traverse it obviously does not matter if the division is performed at the end of each traverse or at the end of an analysis. It follows that bias does not exist if the measurement area is a parallelogram and the traverse path is parallel to any face. This restriction on the shape and orientation of the measurement area is not essential in the discussion of randomly chosen lines as estimators of areas because, as we have seen, such lines are consistent estimators and we ordinarily sum intercepts over a considerable number of them before calculating the composition ratio.

It does provide us with a useful way of thinking about our occasional thin sections as samples of hand specimens, however, for the argument is easily generalized to three dimensions. Bankier demonstrates in this way that any randomly chosen thin section is an unbiased sample of the composition of the rectangular prism from which it is cut. If a diamond saw has been used in preparing the section, for instance, the resulting tablet is presumably a portion of Bankier's prism.

Intuitively, it seems that the argument could be carried beyond this point. A virtual prism may be associated with a possible section cut in any direction whatever from a hand specimen of irregular shape. These prisms may differ somewhat in composition, but each is presumably an unbiased sample of the hand specimen and each section is an unbiased sample of its associated prism. Some way of specifying that the disposition and shape of the bounding surface of the hand specimen are not subject to non-random compositional effects would appear to be the only remaining requirement.

It is thus reasonable to suppose that the bias of randomly chosen thin sections as samples of volumes is small or negligible. At present, however, we have no way of showing that this is necessarily so.

2

The modal analysis
of banded rocks_____

1. INTRODUCTION

What we shall rather loosely term "orientation"—whether the dimensional orientation of individual grains or aggregates, or the segregation (differential or total) of minerals of different species into distinct bands—has always been the *bête noire* of modal analysis. Delesse evidently felt that the difficulties created by it were not critical, for he did analyze oriented rocks and even devised a special definition of "two-dimensional homogeneity" for such materials. The example he set has been neglected, but his careful words of caution have been repeated or paraphrased in almost every subsequent discussion of modal analysis, and what he intended as a warning has gradually assumed the character of an outright injunction.

By a curious irony, the first really practical instrument designed for modal analysis, the Wentworth-Hunt line integrator (see chapter 3), appeared during the great revival of interest in structural geology at the close of the first World War. The elegant work of Cloos, Sander, Schmidt, and their pupils inevitably focused attention on oriented rocks. The striking successes of the new methods had the further incidental effect of making it seem that some type of orientation could be found in almost any rock, provided only that one were willing to look hard enough for it. An analytical procedure thought to be unsound except in "unoriented" or "homogeneous" materials could hardly prosper in such an environment.

The reader will have noted that nothing whatever was said about this problem in the preceding chapter. The question of whether areal proportions lead to consistent estimates of volumetric proportions is entirely a matter of sampling *procedure*; all that is required of material being sampled is that it be sufficiently coarse to permit unambiguous identification of the various mineral grains and ready location of the intersections of their contacts with the surface of the measurement area.

Even if only for psychological reasons, however, we cannot afford to dismiss the subject in this cavalier fashion. Rather, we are obligated to attempt to put it in proper perspective, to show, as Delesse seems to have realized, that the problems created by orientation, however perplexing, are essentially special and practical. This obligation places us in a rather difficult position. Modal analyses of rocks showing pronounced dimensional orientation are occasionally made, and even more occasionally they are published. Yet no satisfactory study of their accuracy and precision, either theoretical or experimental, has so far appeared in print.[1]

The types of orientation with which we are concerned are lineation, foliation, and banding. The first signifies the parallel or subparallel alignment of grains or aggregates, the second a tendency for either the long axes of elongate grains or the broad faces of platy minerals to lie parallel or nearly parallel to a particular plane. For the third type of orientation we use the noncommittal term banding, indicating that the rock is composed of alternating bands of different modal composition. How this banding has developed is none of our concern. The segregation of the mineral constituents of a rock into bands of different composition presents the same problem to the petrographer whether it is brought about by igneous, metamorphic, or sedimentary processes. This is true also of lineation and foliation, either of which may develop in a variety of ways in rocks of very different history.[2]

Considering only the common geometrical elements of the three orientation types, we may regard a foliate rock as a banded rock in which the bands are discontinuous, and lineation may similarly be regarded as a special case of foliation.

At the present time it is not possible to present an exhaustive analysis of the problem; our object in discussing it is primarily to provide a corrective to the false pessimism that it has aroused, and we shall attempt to accomplish this without encouraging false optimism. In order to conserve space we shall treat only the case of true banding, since this presents the

---

[1] A start in this direction has been made. See D. M. Shaw and W. D. Harrison, Determination of the mode of a metamorphic rock, *Am. Min.*, vol. 40, pp. 614–623, 1955.

[2] The proposed definitions of the three "types" of orientation conform well enough with standard usage in chemical petrology but overlap and conflict with the more complex definitions of structural petrology in a rather confusing fashion. It is to be remembered, however, that neither lattice orientation nor patterns generated by joints, rock cleavages, etc., create any difficulty in modal analysis. The structures with which we are concerned are solely those generated by dimensional orientation of individual grains or granular aggregates. This eliminates most of the conflict with regard to lineation and foliation, but some structural geologists, alas, would not admit that banding—often called foliation in chemical petrology—is in any sense an orientation.

most severe challenge to the ordinary techniques of modal analysis. At an early stage of the discussion we shall introduce a very simple model characterized by geometrically perfect orientation, something never found in rocks. It is to be remembered that the difficulties we are about to discuss do not arise in the modal analyses of rocks in which orientation is weak or lacking. The perfect banding of our model will thus be an advantage rather than a handicap; such a model presents us with the situation at its worst.

2. SELECTION OF THE PLANE OF MEASUREMENT IN A BANDED ROCK

In what plane of the banded rock shall we make our measurements? This question has been answered many times, usually in the same way. In a sense, the banded rock consists of two kinds of items, and since the items of each class are not strictly identical—bands of the same type varying, perhaps considerably, in both width and composition—it is obviously advantageous to include as many of them as possible in any particular measurement area. The measurement area should therefore be at a high angle, and preferably normal, to the plane of the banding.

The normal orientation is usually suggested as if it were the only one which could give an accurate result; indeed, this is the way in which it was originally proposed by Delesse. From the argument of the preceding chapter, however, it is clear that repeated random sampling *at any angle to any structure element* will ultimately give the same result as repeated random sampling in the normal orientation. The amount of repetition required to achieve a given precision will generally be less for samples taken normal to the banding than for those taken in any other position or combination of positions. The normal orientation is no more proper than any other; it is simply more efficient.

3. INCLINATION OF THE MEASUREMENT AREA TO THE TRACE OF THE BANDING

The decision to take the plane of measurement normal (or nearly normal) to the plane of the banding is easily reached and far from novel. The question of how to orient the measurement area in this plane is more troublesome. Since most modern thin sections are of rectangular outline and most instruments designed for modal analysis trace out sets of equidistant lines or point sequences parallel to one edge of the thin section, we shall suppose that the measurement area is a rectangle of length l and width w. At what inclination, ω, to the trace of the banding shall we orient this rectangle? Or, more generally, how do the size and inclination of the measurement area affect its composition?

The general solution to this problem is a matter of considerable difficulty.

For a given inclination, for instance, a small measurement area is not necessarily a worse sample than a large one, and an area of intermediate size may be better than either. Further, an area which provides a perfect sample at certain values of ω will certainly not do so at others. By a simple if rather extended exercise in plane geometry, however, we can show that, even if the number of bands per measurement area is rather small, the sampling problem is far less serious than is ordinarily supposed, and that as the number of bands per measurement area increases it becomes negligible. For our immediate purpose nothing more is required.

Taken in any plane but that of the banding, a thin section of a banded rock will consist of a series of alternating parallel bands. We shall suppose that these bands are of exactly equal width and of only two types, A and B. The parent specimen thus contains 50 per cent, by volume, of each band type, and an indefinitely extended plane through this specimen at any non-zero angle to the plane of the banding contains 50 per cent, by area, of each band type.

As a model of such a plane we may use a piece of lined composition paper, the lines representing traces of the contacts between bands of the two types so that the projected band width, t, which is the same for both band types, is simply the distance between the lines. In order to study the effect of inclination on the composition of a rectangular measurement area, we rotate a rectangle of length l and width w about an origin situated on any band contact (or line of the paper). For convenience we set one corner of the rectangle at this origin. The model is shown in Fig. 5. In general, the measurement area will contain a small excess of one band type over the other, but by construction it is easily shown that at a number of values of ω this excess vanishes, and the measurement area has exactly the same composition as the parent fabric. This situation holds if any one of the following conditions is satisfied:

(a) $l = w \tan \omega$ regardless of the band width t. In this case the diagonal of the measurement area lies along a band contact.

(b) w is an even integral multiple of $t/\sin \omega$, regardless of the length of l.

(c) l is an even integral multiple of $t/\cos \omega$, regardless of the length of w.

(d) l is any integral multiple of $t/\cos \omega$, and w is any integral multiple of $t/\sin \omega$.

(e) The quantity $(l^2 + w^2)^{1/2}$—the diagonal of the measurement area—is an even integral multiple of $t/\cos (\omega + \theta)$ where $\theta = \tan^{-1} (w/l)$ and $(\omega + \theta) < 90°$.

(f) The quantity $(l^2 + w^2)^{1/2}$ is an even integral multiple of $t/\sin (\omega + \theta - 90°)$ where θ is as defined in (e) and $(\omega + \theta) > 90°$. (If $(\omega + \theta) = 90°$ exactly, rule (a) applies, and there is no need to specify the dimensions of the measurement rectangle.)

Relations (*a–f*), which the interested reader may wish to verify on a sheet of his own note paper, will of course only rarely characterize an entire measurement area. But any measurement area may be subdivided into subareas, in each of which one or other of these conditions is satisfied, plus a remainder which satisfies none of them. The remainder contains an excess of one band over the other, and this excess is readily located, once

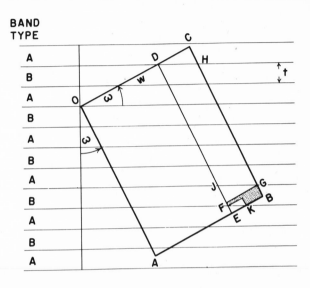

Fig. 5. Rectangular measurement area (*OABC*) inclined at angle ω to a banded fabric.

more by construction. In Fig. 5, for instance, the subarea *OAED* satisfies condition (*b*), and the excess is accordingly located in the remainder *DEBC*. In this remainder the parallelogram *DJGH* contains equal areas of the two band types, so that the excess for the entire figure is no larger than the difference *JEBG* — *DHC*, and by construction this is the rectangle *EBGF*, at the lower right corner. In this rectangle the small triangle *EKF*, in band type *A*, balances an equal area in the adjacent band type *B*. The full figure thus contains an excess of band type *B* exactly equal to the stippled portion of rectangle *EBGF*.

By simple construction of this sort we can always determine which band type is present in excess in the measurement area, and with careful draftsmanship we can also get a pretty fair notion of the size of the excess. If we wish numerical estimates of the size of the excess, however, we shall have to specify numerical values for *t*, *l*, *w*, and ω; given these we can always calculate the exact size of the excess, but the calculation is often very tedious. As we have no need for a purely symbolic statement of the relation we shall content ourselves with a practical example, one which at first glance would appear to be very unfavorable.

To simplify the calculations we shall take w and l as integral multiples of t, specifically $w = 3t, l = 5t$, and allow ω to vary in the range $0 < \omega < 180°$. The values $w = 3, l = 5$, are chosen for two reasons. In the first place, the ratio of length to width of the very common 24×40 mm. cover-slip is $3 : 5$. Second, if either edge of the measurement area happens to parallel the trace of the banding, the measurement area grossly misrepresents the composition of the fabric. For either band the true value μ is 50 per cent, whether by area or by volume. If, in our example, l is parallel to the trace of the banding, the composition of the measurement area will be 66.7 per cent of one band type and 33.3 per cent of the other; if w lies parallel to the trace of the banding the composition of the measurement area will be 60 per cent of one band type and 40 per cent of the other, still a sizable misestimate. (In passing we may note that for the standard 24×40 mm. cover-slip the dimensions of our hypothetical measurement area indicate a band thickness of $t = 8$ mm., and this is large enough so that separate thin sections of each band type could be cut; under many circumstances it might be preferable to do this, and estimate the relative abundance of the bands by separate measurements on a large polished slab.)

Given numerical values for t, w, and l we can calculate the excess for any value of ω, but the calculation is particularly simple if, in addition to the origin, one (or more) of the other corners of the measurement area falls on a band boundary. In the course of a $180°$ rotation this will happen 24 times for our 3×5 rectangle; no fewer than 11 of these "integral intersections" satisfy some one of rules $(a–f)$, so that for 11 different values of ω in the range $0 \leqslant \omega \leqslant 180°$ the excess vanishes and the composition of the measurement area is exactly the same as that of the parent fabric. Taking ω as the angle between w and the trace of the banding (see Fig. 5), these "no-excess" positions are located at: $15.78°, 36.87°, 38.99°, 41.81°, 59.04°, 66.42°, 79.08°, 102.30°, 113.58°, 138.19°, 143.13°$.

The locations of the 24 "integral intersections" may be determined from Fig. 6, which shows the path traced out by each corner of the measurement area, $OPQR$, in a $180°$ rotation. The inner semicircle marks the locus of the point P, and along it lie the integral intersections which satisfy condition (b). The median semicircle performs a similar function for Q, and along it are marked integral positions satisfying condition (c). The outer semicircle marks the locus of R, and on it occur integral positions satisfying conditions (a), (e), and (f). For the first intersection of type (b), $\omega = \sin^{-1}(2/3)$. For the first of type (c), $\omega = \cos^{-1}(4/5)$. For the single intersection of type (*a*), $\omega + \theta = 90$ and $\omega = \tan^{-1}(5/3)$; for the first intersection of type (*e*), $\omega = \cos^{-1}(4/\sqrt{34}) - \tan^{-1}(3/5)$.[3]

In similar fashion ω can be calculated for the other integral positions. At those which lie on odd-numbered band contacts, as well as for all values of θ at which no corner is distant an integral multiple of *t* from the origin, the measurement area will in general contain some excess of one

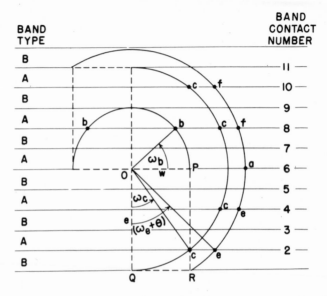

Fig. 6. Location of the integral intersections for a measurement area of
length $l = 5t$ and width $w = 3t$.

band type over the other. We proceed to show, by results for the odd-integral positions, that this excess is ordinarily rather small. Figure 7 gives a graphical statement of it for each of the odd-integral positions in the region $0 < \omega < 180°$. The ω values shown on the diagram have been calculated in the fashion already described. From them and the assigned dimensions of *l* and *w* (5 and 3, respectively) we can calculate the size of the shaded area, or excess, in each figure. Denoting this area as *e*, the quantity we seek is $e/2$ as a proportion or percentage of the entire measurement area, or

$$z = |\bar{x}_b - \mu| = |\bar{x}_a - \mu| = \frac{e}{2lw} \tag{2.1}$$

[3] It will be noted that all the "no-excess" positions occur on even-numbered band contacts. The numbering scheme has been chosen as a reminder that each such point is distant from the origin by an *even integral* multiple of the projected band width. "No-excess" positions satisfying condition (*d*) do not occur in a measurement area of these dimensions.

since our concern is the discrepancy between the amount of either band type in the measurement area ($\bar{x}_a$ or $\bar{x}_b$) and its amount in the parent fabric

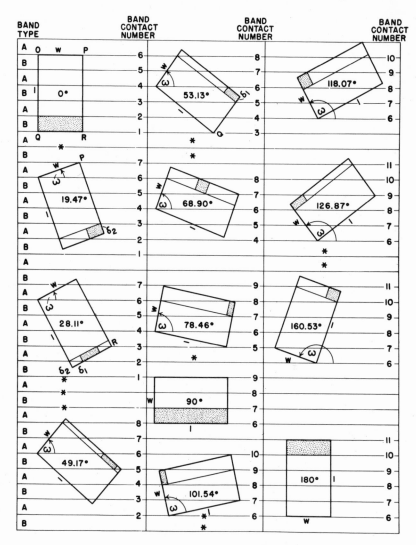

Fig. 7. Isolation of remainder and excess areas in a 3×5 measurement area at odd-numbered integral intersections. (Excess shaded. Asterisks show location of no-excess positions.)

($\mu = 0.5$ or 50 per cent).

Beginning with the first odd intersection of OP in Fig. 7, we have that

$$\delta_2 = l - \frac{(l-1)}{\cos \omega} = 5 - \frac{4}{\cos \omega} \tag{2.2}$$

and the area of the complete remainder is

$$A_R = w\delta_2 = 3\left(5 - \frac{4}{\cos \omega}\right) \tag{2.3}$$

The balanced (unshaded) portion has dimensions δ_2 and $\delta_2/\tan \omega$, so that its area is

$$A_B = \frac{\delta_2{}^2}{\tan \omega} \tag{2.4}$$

The shaded portion, or excess, is accordingly

$$e = A_R - A_B = w\delta_2 - \frac{\delta_2{}^2}{\tan \omega} \tag{2.5}$$

and finally

$$z = \frac{1}{2lw}\left(w\delta_2 - \frac{\delta_2{}^2}{\tan \omega}\right) = \frac{\delta_2}{2lw}\left(w - \frac{\delta_2}{\tan \omega}\right) = 0.0221 \tag{2.6}$$

The measurement area thus contains 52.2 per cent of band type A and 47.8 per cent of band type B.

Considering next the odd integral intersections of the end point of the diagonal R we note that the first occurs at $\omega = 0$, where $z = 0.100$ and the measurement area contains 60 per cent of band type B. The next odd position is at band contact 3, where

$$\delta_1 = 3 - \frac{1}{\sin \omega}, \quad \delta_2 = 5 - \frac{4}{\cos \omega} \tag{2.7}$$

and we can calculate z directly as

$$z = \frac{\delta_2}{30}(3 - 2\delta_1) = 0.0195 \tag{2.8}$$

so that the measurement area contains 51.95 per cent of band type A and 48.05 per cent of band type B.

Finally, we note that the first odd intersection of Q, like that of R, occurs at $\omega = 0$. At the next odd intersection (band contact 3, as for R), we have from Fig. 7

$$\delta_1 = 3 - \frac{2}{\sin \omega} \tag{2.9}$$

for the w component of the excess. Parallel to l its length is

$$\frac{1}{\cos \omega} - \delta_1 \tan \omega$$

and, accordingly,

$$e = \delta_1 \left(\frac{1}{\cos \omega} - \delta_1 \tan \omega \right) \tag{2.10}$$

$$z = \frac{\delta_1}{30} \left(\frac{1}{\cos \omega} - \delta_1 \tan \omega \right) = 0.0164 \tag{2.11}$$

so that the measurement area contains 51.64 per cent of band type B and 48.36 per cent of band type A.

The results of these and similar calculations for the other intersections are drawn together in Table 2.1, in which z is listed as negative if the measurement area contains an excess of B over A.

TABLE 2.1. INCLINATION (ω) AND PERCENTAGE VALUE OF EXCESS ($100z$) FOR ALL INTEGRAL INTERSECTIONS OF A 3×5 MEASUREMENT AREA ROTATED THROUGH $180°$ ABOUT ONE CORNER ON A BAND CONTACT

$\omega°$	$100z$
0	−10.00
15.78	0
19.47	+2.21
28.11	+1.95
36.87	0
39.00	0
41.81	0
49.17	−1.35
53.13	−1.64
59.04	0
66.42	0
68.90	−1.57
78.46	−1.02
79.08	0
90.00	+16.67
101.54	+1.02
102.30	0
113.58	0
118.07	+1.84
126.87	+1.67
138.19	0
143.13	0
160.53	+2.18
180.00	+10.00

Variation in the composition of the measurement area is continuous, but, as the table shows, the function that governs it must be extremely complex. Fortunately, we do not require exhaustive information about this function; our only object is to show that the sampling problem posed by banding is not insuperable, and this is easily done. Figure 8 is a graph of the data of Table 2.1 for $0 \leqslant \omega \leqslant 90°$. The line connecting the points

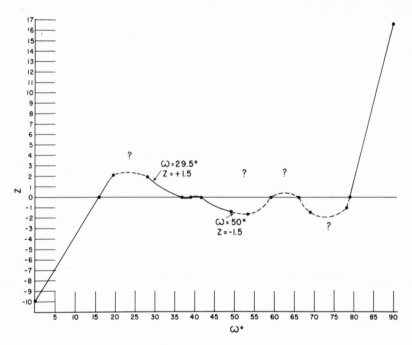

Fig. 8. Curve connecting z values for integral intersections of a 3×5 measurement area in the region $0 \leqslant \omega \leqslant 90°$, rotated about one corner situated on a band contact. Data of Table 2.1.

is partly solid, partly dotted; we have said nothing about whether or not z is a maximum (or minimum) at the odd-integral intersections. Sometimes the integral intersections mark maxima or minima; sometimes they do not. In the central region (between the first and second question marks) the portion of the curve shown as a solid line has been tested by rather extensive calculations. The curlicue connecting the three "no-excess" points in the center of this region is real, though if drawn strictly to scale it would hardly show. On either side of the triplet the curve is very nearly linear, and the slope of the branch on the left is very nearly equal to that of the branch on the right. Thus if ω is chosen simply at random in the region $30° < \omega < 50°$ z will be essentially uniformly distributed about 0 with $\sigma = ca\ 3/\sqrt{12}$ or 0.87 per cent. Because of the flat central region, extending over about 5°, the standard deviation of z will actually be somewhat smaller than this.

Now the requirement that one corner of the measurement area coincide with a band contact is not difficult to satisfy, and neither is the condition that ω be chosen simply at random over an interval of 20°. If these conditions are satisfied the banding introduces no bias and makes only a small contribution to the random variation which, in a later chapter, we shall define as analytical error. We conclude that our perfectly banded model can indeed be adequately sampled by a rectangular measurement area even if the edges of the rectangle are only 3 and 5 times the band width.[4]

4. Effect of Dimensions of the Measurement Area on the Size of the Excess

As we have already pointed out, for a given value of ω a large measurement area is not necessarily a more exact sample of the parent fabric than a small one. In fact, there will always be particular values of ω at which the opposite holds. It will nevertheless be true generally that a large area is more efficient than a small one; the larger either edge of the measurement area, the more numerous will be the "no-excess" positions generated during its rotation and the smaller the departures from exact balance at inclinations intermediate between these positions. As the dimensions of the measurement area increase relative to the band width the slope of the portions adjacent to the flat central region of the curve in Fig. 8 becomes gentler. As in many situations of this sort, the improvement produced by the first increases in size (really in the *number* of band widths per side of the rectangle) may be quite startling. If, in our example, the band width is halved, for instance, so that the edges of the rectangle are $6t$ and $10t$, respectively—values not at all unlikely in thin sections of low-grade metamorphic rocks—*every one of the 24 ω values listed in Table 2.1 designates a "no-excess" position,* and the value of z at the other 31 integral intersections is always less than 1 per cent and nearly always less than 0.5 per cent.

5. A Model for Band Types of Different Thicknesses

The only way in which we can permit the composition of our model to vary from an even balance between the two band types is by specifying that one type of band is thicker than the other.

[4] A more indirect geometrical characterization of the excess greatly simplifies the calculation of z for the case under consideration. In appendix 2 interested readers will find an outline of the procedure and a table listing the variation of z with ω in the critical region of the curve shown in Fig. 8.

All the plane geometry of the preceding section is predicated on a single width, t, common to both band types. It can readily be adapted to accommodate *random* variation in this width. If we specify that the *mean* thickness t and its standard deviation are the same in both bands the situation is little changed. At each ω value the expected or long-run average value for the composition is exactly what we found by supposing t constant. A random variation in t which is independent of band type contributes to analytical error but does not affect the consistency of the procedure; it reduces the efficiency of our estimate but does not change the thing we are estimating.

A *systematic* difference between t_a and t_b, however, introduces real difficulties, and without such a difference the composition of our parent sample may not depart from an even balance between the two band types. Fortunately, our lined-paper model is easily adjusted to permit such variation. All that is necessary is a redefinition of the distance between the lines. This distance is now $t_a = t_b = t$. If we specify instead that it represents a *full cycle*, $t_a + t_b$, the parent specimen is free to have any composition it chooses. Space does not permit a full examination of the consequences of this change in definition, but the interested reader may wish to investigate the subject himself. Both the locations of the "no-excess" positions and the rules for isolating a remainder area containing the excess require some modification. Except in special cases the diagonal of the measurement area is of no use in locating the "no-excess" positions, but *every* integral intersection of the end points of l and w now locates such a position, instead of only alternate intersections. (Similarly, the diagonal is rarely of use in isolating the remainder, but *all* intersections of the cycle contacts with l or w serve this purpose.) The net result is an increase in the number of "no-excess" positions and a more uniform angular distribution of them.[5]

6. ANALYSIS OF A BANDED MEASUREMENT AREA

We thus have every reason to suppose that the sampling problems occasioned by banding are considerably less serious than is ordinarily believed, and that most if not all of them can be eliminated by careful work. How shall we set about the analysis of an efficiently selected banded measurement area? In such a measurement area, as we have seen, the trace of the banding will be inclined at a considerable angle to either edge of the measurement area. And every modern machine designed for modal analysis traces out lines or sequences of points parallel to one of the

---

[5] If we generalize a little further, and set the distance between lines equal to $\sum_{1}^{n} t_k$, the new model also applies to rocks containing more than two types of bands.

edges of the measurement area. (In a sense, the point counters trace out point sequences parallel to both edges of the measurement area.) Traverses are ordinarily spaced out at a constant interval, and if the traverse path were parallel or nearly parallel to the trace of the banding this might sometimes introduce serious biases. The possibility is much reduced, however, by the inclination between the trace of the banding and the edge of the measurement area. It may be excluded by abandoning the fixed traverse interval, which is appropriate in the absence of orientation, and using instead a traverse interval purposely randomized. Randomization of the traverse interval is readily accomplished in any instrument equipped with a vernier reading to tenths of millimeters along the direction of the traverse normal.

In a measurement area 24 mm. wide, for instance, an analysis made with a fixed 1-mm. traverse interval consists of 24 traverses. For convenience, let us suppose that the first of these traverses falls exactly at 0.0 mm. on the traverse normal. The next will lie at 1.0, the third at 2.0, and so on. In order to randomize the sequence we fix the tenths place of each vernier setting by means of a table of random numbers. Designating these as $r_1, r_2, r_3, \cdots r_{24}$, the successive traverse sites will then be at $0.r_1$ mm. on the vernier instead of 0.0, $1.r_2$ instead of 1.0, and so on. An actual sampling of this sort gives:

0.2	3.0	6.8	9.7	12.4	15.3	18.4	21.8
1.6	4.1	7.6	10.8	13.0	16.5	19.0	22.2
2.3	5.3	8.3	11.9	14.5	17.7	20.4	23.6

A new drawing is to be made for each analysis, whether of the same or a different thin section. The traverse sites must of course be located by the vernier instead of whatever spacing device is normally used. (In most instruments the vernier is the spacing device.)

The conventional, regular spacing places a traverse *at* every millimeter. The suggested alternative places a traverse at a site randomly chosen from ten possibilities *within* each millimeter. It substitutes a "stratified-random" sample for the "systematic" sample of common practice. If we chose to do so, we could also replace the latter with a "simple-random" sample, in which the full vernier reading, instead of only the tenths place, would be fixed by a drawing from a table of random numbers. In terms of efficiency, stratified-random sampling is usually considerably superior to simple-random sampling. In the present situation it should also be at least as efficient as the systematic sampling (traverse spacing) of ordinary practice. Without loss—and possibly even with some gain—of precision, it eliminates biases which might sometimes arise from periodic relations between band width and traverse interval.

7. Conclusion

This extended discussion falls far short of a complete and logically rigorous guide to the modal analysis of strongly oriented rocks. It will have served its purpose if it provides an antidote to the habitual and largely unwarranted pessimism about the feasibility of such analysis. Probably stemming originally from careless paraphrases and mis- or overstatements of Delesse's position, this pessimism contains also a heavy burden of traditional inertia and a leavening of the kind of common sense that is so commonly wrong.

The consistence (see chapter 1) of estimates of volumetric proportions based on areal measurements is not in any way influenced by the presence (or absence) of orientation. What *is* affected by orientation is the random analytical error. There is no question that orientation may enlarge (or reduce) this error under some circumstances, and that sometimes the enlargement may be so extreme as to render the procedure unusable. The whole problem of applying modal analysis to oriented rocks is a completely practical matter of estimating the enlargement of analytical error generated by a particular species of orientation, and of learning how to reduce it to suitable dimensions. Our discussion has shown that for one extremely critical species of orientation this problem is probably much less serious than is commonly believed, but it would be misleading in the extreme to suggest that it is either simple or insoluble.

3

Methods of
measuring relative areas
_____in thin sections

In this chapter we shall review briefly the development of techniques and instruments for modal analysis. Although Delesse first proposed the basic relation to which we have assigned his name (eq. 1.12) he developed no instrument specifically designed for modal analysis. His only "practical" contribution was a technique so impractical as to discourage imitation for nearly half a century. In the work of his first professed disciple, Rosiwal, the emphasis is on a supposedly novel geometrical theory which, as we shall soon see, actually assumes the Delesse relation. Like Delesse, Rosiwal developed a technique rather than an instrument.

The modern development of the subject begins with Shand, who did not concern himself about the geometrical basis of the method but designed an instrument which for the first time brought modal analysis into the realm of practical scientific activity.

1. DELESSE, ROSIWAL, SHAND

The contribution of Delesse is curiously uneven. A strong geometrical intuition led him to a perfectly general though unproved statement of the relation between relative expected areas and relative volumes. His treatment of the "cylindrical model" shows that he was acutely aware of the unsatisfactory state of his demonstration, and his tortuous discussion of oriented rocks shows that he either did not appreciate or did not trust the generality of the relation. As we have just seen, even a smattering of elementary statistical analysis permits a more satisfactory derivation of the general Delesse relation. This smattering was not available to Delesse; the language had not been invented and he can hardly be blamed for not knowing it.

The technique by which he actually estimated areas, on the other hand, seems tedious and crude. He first placed a piece of waxed paper over a polished surface and traced on this the outlines of the underlying mineral areas. The pattern was next transferred to tin foil and the various areas cut apart with a tin snips. Scraps of foil representing sections of the same mineral on the original surface were then assembled and weighed. The possibilities of error seem fabulous.

His method predates the common use of thin sections, and Delesse himself worked only on polished surfaces without benefit of microscope. Sorby seems to have been the first to make modal analyses with the aid of the microscope. He made camera lucida drawings of individual microscope fields on "an evenly thick piece of drawing paper," and estimated relative areas on these by the same technique Delesse applied to his tin foil. Joly substituted a graphical summing for the cutting and weighing step. Johanssen finally eliminated the necessity of reproducing the surface pattern by using a planimeter directly on the camera lucida projection; he insists that this is a fairly painless operation, but from his description it would appear to be a formidable task.

The critical defect of all the direct measurement procedures which utilize the microscope is simply that each measurement is confined to a single microscope field. As considerable magnification is usually required for proper identification, the areas of individual sample fields can hardly exceed a few tens of square millimeters. For most rocks, as we shall see, this is an entirely inadequate area.[1] *All* modal analyses depend on the Delesse relation, but only the direct areal measurements may be said to be descendents of the Delesse technique. They are of little importance in modern petrography.

Rosiwal's accomplishment, like that of Delesse, is mixed and difficult to assess fairly. Although his name is generally applied to procedures which are purposely designed to yield estimates of relative areas by means of parallel equidistant traverses, this is not at all the way he thought of his "Gesteinsfaden," and in his work on polished slabs he often used lines which were neither straight nor parallel (see, for instance, Figs. 3 and 4, 1898). He seems to have thought that he had developed a complete substitute for the Delesse relation, but as his measurements had to be made on a plane surface they can estimate the composition of a volume only to the extent that the surface can do so. The Delesse relation is thus a necessary intermediary.[2] Rosiwal's real importance to us is not that he

[1] Sollas actually proposed the use of no less than 24 microscope fields per thin section of the Leinster granite!

[2] The most extensive development of the reasoning underlying the Rosiwal procedure is by Lincoln and Rietz. They cite a theorem of Cavalieri as a geometrical alternative for the proof of the Delesse relation "outlined" by Delesse, and proceed to urge that what

showed us how to dispose of it, as he evidently supposed, but rather that he showed us how to make use of it; this Delesse himself had been unable to do.

We have just noted that Rosiwal's "rock-thread" was not necessarily straight, and that it did not necessarily consist of parallel or orthogonal segments. In thin section, however, the intercept distances were to be measured with an eyepiece micrometer, and this is probably his reason for using a rectangular line grid. He recorded intercept distances for each grain (or mineral species) along each traverse. The amount of paper work must have been immense, and the opportunity for error almost as great as with Delesse's tin snips. The time requirement, although probably somewhat reduced, was certainly excessive. A 4-cm.² thin section of a coarse-grained rock could be done in "einige Stunden"; he mentions that the speed of operation drops off with increase in the number of grain sections per traverse, but how many hours were required for a thin section of a medium- or fine-grained rock he does not say.

The first really substantial improvement in the technique of thin-section analysis, the Shand recording micrometer, was a logical development of the Rosiwal procedure. In this instrument the measuring is done, not in the eyepiece of the microscope, but in the traversing mechanism of the stage. Calibrated wheels are fitted on two opposed threads, and the thin section is drawn across the table of the microscope by rotation of either thread. One thread is used only in traversing an "unknown," the other is used for all other constituents. At the end of each traverse the dial readings are recorded, and at the end of the analysis the differences between successive readings are summed for each dial. The sums of these differences are, respectively, the total traverse path in the unknown $S(U)$, and in the remainder $S(R)$. The desired areal ratio is $S(U)/(S(U) + S(R))$.

The practical advantage of measuring with the traversing mechanism is enormous. In the Rosiwal technique the operator must record the intercept for each grain. In the Shand technique a record is made only at the end of each traverse. The Shand stage eliminates completely the fatigue and tension accompanying prolonged use of the eyepiece micrometer. A single traverse with the Shand stage requires no more than a couple of minutes, and a full analysis for one constituent can be completed in a half-hour to an hour, depending on the width of the thin section and the distance between traverses.

---

is true of the relation between areas and volumes is also true of the relation between lines and areas. The only difficulty is that the theorem is inapplicable; it holds only if the cross-sectional areas of two solids are equal at every level, and this generally is untrue of mineral grains in a rock. The Lincoln-Reitz argument does not tell us whether the results of modal analyses are physically interpretable as volume percentages or should be regarded merely as reproducible indices of unknown meaning.

The Shand micrometer is open to criticism in two respects, one purely mechanical, the other reflecting the generally unsatisfactory state of the theory of the subject. The mechanical defect is simply that a single analysis produces a result for only one constituent, so that a complete repetition of the traversing is necessary for each mineral of which an estimate is desired.

The other major defect is the lack of a device permitting either random or systematic selection of traverses. Mechanically, of course, this is trifling; a millimeter scale along the traverse normal would have done the job, and Shand says as much. What is important is that it did not seem worth doing. Rosiwal thought he had bypassed the necessity of estimating areal ratios; all that mattered was the relative lengths of lines. His only specification of what we call traverse interval was that it should not be less than the "grain size," and this specification carries over into the original description of the Shand micrometer. Although his diagrams indicate that when he used parallel lines he did in fact space them equally, he nowhere indicates that this is either necessary or desirable. Nor does Shand. Now it is clear that, unless the traverses are either systematically or randomly spaced, they will not yield consistent estimates of areal ratios. Rosiwal insisted on regarding the "Gesteinsfaden" as a sample of the rock rather than of the rock-surface on which it was drawn. Under his influence petrographers gradually lost sight of the Delesse relation, and of the fact that it could work only if the numerator and denominator of the left side of eq. (1.12) were what would today be called consistent estimates of areas *in a plane*.

2. CONTINUOUS LINE INTEGRATORS

The continuous line integrators now common are all direct descendents and elaborations of the Shand micrometer stage. Wentworth was the first to describe an instrument which would permit simultaneous analysis for several constituents. In the Hurlbut instrument the traversing and tallying mechanisms are motor driven. It is notable that the original Wentworth micrometer, like the Shand stage, failed to include any mechanism permitting either random or systematic selection of traverses. The omission is particularly curious in the Wentworth stage for Wentworth himself recommended the equal spacing of traverses which has now become standard practice.

The published descriptions of the Wentworth-Hunt and Hurlbut stages will be readily available to most geological readers. In the Leitz and Zeiss catalogues the reader will find descriptions of remarkably expensive instruments similar to the Wentworth-Hunt.[3]

[3] Also of even more expensive motor-driven ones similar to the Hurlbut. One of the latter appeared on the market while the description of the Hurlbut stage was in press.

In the instruments so far described the linkage between tallying and traversing mechanism exists only when a particular key (or knob) is actually in use.   In an instrument described by Dollar, on the other hand, the tallying drums are always linked to the traversing mechanism and are kept from rotating by small friction brakes.   The operator works the traversing wheel with one hand, and with the other he depresses keys assigned to various minerals; depression of a key releases the brake and permits the drum to turn; release of the key restores the braking action and stops the drum.

3. Point Counters

The substitution of points for lines in the estimation of areas is a relatively recent development.   A symmetrical, but not necessarily isotropic, point grid is cast over the measurement area, and the mineral underlying each point is identified.   In practice, of course, the slide moves across the microscope table, and the mineral underlying the cross hair intersection at each stop is identified and tallied.

In 1933 A. A. Glagolev published a description of what appears to be first point counter designed for petrographic analysis; the following year a translation of part of his description was published in this country but attracted little attention.   The Glagolev counter has never been offered commercially either here or in Europe.   In the Glagolev instrument a cable similar to the cable release on a camera joins the counting box to a sledge mounted on the microscope table.   Depression of any one of the keys of the counter box automatically translates the sledge to the next point on the grid and adds a tally to the appropriate counter.   Barringer has more recently substituted a solenoid-activated armature for the cable of the Glagolev instrument, and a thread for the sledge.

· In 1949 a simple and relatively inexpensive point counter was described by Chayes.   In this instrument, for the first time since they were brought together in the Shand stage, the tallying and traversing mechanisms are again completely separated.   The point grid is generated by means of spring clips riding on notched wheels mounted at the ends of the thread and pinion of a standard mechanical stage.   In the American Optical Co. model the tension of the spring clips is controlled by set screws, and with these backed off the mechanical stage operates in normal fashion, with no clicking action.   The counting unit is a block such as is ordinarily used for biological work or menu-counting in cafeterias.   That the operator is required to use both hands has occasioned some criticism.   A number of modifications of the instrument have been suggested and tried, but only two of these have so far appeared in print (Rosenfeld, Chayes).

Ford has described as a point counter a cleverly designed instrument which is more nearly a line integrator. A notched pinion wheel turning with the traversing thread activates a switch which conducts impulses to a counting box in which electromagnetic counters are mounted in parallel. Each counter is controlled by a key which the operator depresses at the appropriate time. Ford has designed the machine to register a count for every translation of 50 to 100 μ, so that the "point" spacing is of the same order as the "continuous" line measurements that can be made with the vernier of an ordinary mechanical stage. The keyboard is operated with one hand; the traversing of the stage is performed by the other. One may wonder whether the average analyst's coordination is such that the counting error will bear any resemblance to the kind of precision expected from the enormous number of "points" generated in the course of an analysis.

The James Swift Co. has recently announced a "servo-operated traversing carriage . . . coupled to an electrical recording or counting unit." The instrument has not been described in the technical press, and the company's brochure contains no wiring diagram. It also fails to mention whether the stage operates on a thread or a sledge. In principle, the instrument seems to be closely analogous to the original Glagolev point counter; depression of any one of the tabulating keys translates the stage to the next point. Since there is no reversing switch, the carriage must be returned manually at the end of each traverse.

The popularity of the point counter is rapidly increasing; it is probably safe to say that, in this country at least, as many modes are now being done by point count as by line integration.

4

The reproducibility
_____of thin-section analyses: I

1. THE IMPORTANCE OF CONSISTENCE

The reader unfamiliar with the terminology of elementary statistics will perhaps have wondered why we made such a fuss, in chapters 1 and 2, about the generality of the Delesse relation. When all is said and done, even if the areal composition of a randomly chosen thin section *is* a consistent estimator of volumetric composition, every geologist can think of occasions in which it would certainly be a pretty poor one. The discussion in chapter 1, however, shows that this poorness is of a special kind, the kind we can often eradicate by proper experimental design.

Had we discovered that thin-section analysis was essentially inconsistent, we would have no right to suppose that correct volumetric ratios could be obtained in this way, and would be forced to conclude that differences between observed and true values were fortuitous and unpredictable. In varying degrees of severity, this is about the position taken not only in text and reference books, but actually in many of the specialized papers on the subject. It is this unfounded fear which sentenced modal analysis to a very minor role in the development of petrography. As late as 1919 Johanssen could seriously recommend his planimeter because it could be built for less than twenty-five dollars, the estimated cost of the Shand recording micrometer. Yet by this time literally thousands of full chemical analyses had been made, Washington's and Osann's Tables had appeared, and all over the country petrographers who presumably could not afford twenty-five dollars for an accessory which would permit them to run any number of modes were managing to find and spend at least that much for each chemical analysis they purchased. The justification for many of these analyses, needless to say, was that they would lead, in one way or other, to estimates of mineralogical composition.

What the Delesse relation tells us is that, provided certain simple rules of sampling are observed, areal measurements made in thin section are theoretically sound and unimpeachable estimates of volumetric proportions. The most important and supposedly insoluble problem of modal analysis simply does not exist. From the work of chapter 1 we know that if our estimates are based on a sufficient number of analyses they are estimates of the parameters we wish to learn about. Now we must turn to a study of their variability.

At the lower level this is obviously a discussion of error and of ways to reduce it, and such a discussion will occupy most of the rest of this work. Even in a discipline as simple as modal analysis the forms and types of error are numerous, and where we should stop calling them error and begin to apply some more dignified name is a matter of taste. We begin with an analysis of the simplest of all variations, one we can all agree to call error—the reproducibility of analyses on the same thin section.

2. THE CONTINUOUS LINE INTEGRATOR

Not much can be said concerning the reproducibility inherent in the continuous line integrator. Only a fragmentary examination is possible since no properly planned experimental study seems to have been made. What work has been done (compare, for instance, Chayes, 1946 and 1949) suggests that with a traverse interval of 1 mm. the error of the Hurlbut and Wentworth instruments is about comparable to that of a point count of a thousand points. The continuous line integrators as a group are likely to differ more in performance characteristics than the point counter, however, and it is probably just as well to avoid extensive speculation about the error of the process as such. What counts is the combination of process, instrument, and operator.

3. THE POINT COUNTER

In the discussion of Fig. 1, chapter 1, we argued that the probability p of a point chosen simply at random in the area $(B + W)$ lying also in B is equal to $A_B/(A_B + A_W)$. Since it must fall in W if it does not fall in B, the probability of its *not* falling in B is

$$q = \frac{A_W}{A_B + A_W} = 1 - p \qquad (4.1)$$

In any actual tallying procedure we add one tally, perhaps by punching a particular key, each time a point in B is chosen, and refrain from punching this particular key each time a chosen point lies outside B. We may say then that we are "observing" a quantity, X, which has the value 1 whenever a point lies in B, and the value 0 whenever a point does not lie in B.   The frequency distribution of X is

X	0	1
$f(X)$	q	p

The population mean will be

$$\mu = \Sigma Xf(x) = (0)(q) + (1)(p) = p \qquad (4.2)[1]$$

If the points are "drawn" in batches of n, we record only the sum of the X's, $S(X)$.   But obviously

$$\mu_{S(X)} = np \qquad (4.3)$$

and if we reduce the result to a percentage basis we have since $\bar{x} = (1/n)S(X)$

$$\mu_{\bar{x}} = \frac{1}{n} \mu_{S(X)} = p \qquad (4.4)$$

Whether we draw the points in batches of the same or different size, each drawing estimates the same population mean.   However, the variance of the estimate varies inversely with the number of points n on which it is based.   From the frequency distribution we can readily calculate the population variance, or variance attaching to an estimate based on batches of size $n = 1$.

By definition, this is

$$\sigma^2 = \Sigma(X - \mu)^2 f(X)$$
$$= (0 - p)^2 q + (1 - p)^2 p$$
$$= pq \qquad (4.5)$$

Accordingly, for $n > 1$,

$$\sigma_n^2 = \frac{1}{n} \sigma_1^2 = \frac{pq}{n} \qquad (4.6)$$

and the standard deviation of an estimate of p based on n points is, in percentage of the whole,

$$\sigma_n = 100 \sqrt{\frac{pq}{n}} \qquad (4.7)$$

---

[1] Whenever possible we shall follow standard statistical practice by using Roman letters for sample values or *statistics* and Greek letters for true values or *population parameters*.

From eq. (4.7) it is clear that, for fixed n, σ is symmetrical about a maximum at $p = 0.5$, and that, for a given p, σ varies inversely as $\sqrt{n}$. It is of far greater importance, though perhaps not so obvious, that for n reasonably large—of about the order encountered in modal analysis—σ is rather insensitive to large differences in p and fairly sizeable differences in n. Table 4.1 shows σ in percentage, calculated for pertinent values of n and p. The theoretical counting error is *not* the same, for instance, at $p = 0.5$, $n = 1400$, as it is at $p = 0.2$, $n = 1600$; in the first case it is 1.3, in the second 1.0. If these were sample estimates based on equal numbers of observations, however, it would be exceedingly difficult to establish that they were drawn from different populations. A 95 per cent assurance that this was so would require no fewer than 40 items in each sample; a 99 per cent assurance would call for 80. A difference this hard to establish is scarcely likely to be of much practical concern. Estimates of the counting error have been the primary objective of one rather extensive test and the byproduct of three others. To varying extent, all four testing procedures take advantage of the insensitivity of σ to small differences in n and rather large ones in p.

TABLE 4.1. σ IN PERCENTAGE OF THE WHOLE FOR PERTINENT COMBINATIONS OF n AND p

n	p			
	0.20	0.30	0.40	0.50
1000	1.3	1.5	1.6	1.6
1400	1.1	1.3	1.3	1.3
1500	1.0	1.2	1.3	1.3
1600	1.0	1.1	1.2	1.2
2000	0.9	1.0	1.1	1.1

The simplest and strongest test of reproducibility would seem to be manifold analysis of a single thin section, but extreme replication often leads to very unrealistic estimates of reproducibility. The observed variation means little unless the replicates can be regarded as independent and random. Even in destructive tests, where a small portion of the sample is consumed in each run, it is not always easy to arrange replications which are genuinely independent. In our case the analyses would have to be run on the same slide with the same instrument. Obviously, only a few different settings are possible; with proper arrangement of the sequence of analyses they may be regarded as being "chosen" independently and at

random.   Repetitions of the same traverse path, however, are not independent replications, since our interest is in the counting error attached to
analyses of the whole measurement area, not that of any particular
traverse path.   All but the first few replications would almost inevitably
follow closely paths traced out before.   If the distribution of mineral
sections along these paths differed widely, we might seriously overestimate
the reproducibility error.   Considering the systematic nature of the
traversing, however, it is far more likely that the successive paths would
differ little from each other.   If this were so, we should almost certainly
grossly *underestimate* the reproducibility error, as is commonly true where
the independence and random selection of the replicates are not assured.

This leaves us in something of a dilemma, for, if reproducibility is not
to be tested on the same slide, information concerning it must be obtained
from analyses of different slides, and p is not necessarily the same even
among thin sections cut from the same hand specimen.   It is for this
reason that the comparative insensitivity of σ to changes in p is so useful;
neither rather large shifts in p from specimen to specimen, nor small
differences in n occasioned by small differences in available measurement
area from slide to slide, will seriously influence our estimates of σ.   All
we need is some scheme which will permit us to concentrate on differences
between replicates without interference from the real differences between
slides.   There are many ways in which this can be done.   Perhaps the
most direct is simply to work only with the differences which interest
us.   Suppose, for instance, that we make duplicate analyses of each of a
series of thin sections.   From each slide we thus accumulate a difference
for each constituent.   The variance of a set of differences is the mean of
the sum of the squared deviations, or

$$s_d{}^2 = \frac{1}{n} \sum_{i=1}^{n} (X_i - \mu)^2 \tag{4.8}$$

where s is the standard deviation, n is the number of thin sections in the
sample, X is an individual difference, and μ is the true (or population)
difference.   In our case $\mu = 0$, for each difference is taken between
duplicates run on the same slide, and the slides do not change during the
test.   We have at once, therefore, that

$$s_d{}^2 = \frac{1}{n} \sum_{i=1}^{n} (X_i)^2 \tag{4.9}$$

As a result of the experimental design the variance of a difference is here
the sum of two independent variances which are equal to each other and
to the square of the reproducibility error of a single analysis, or

$$s_d^2 = 2s_a^2 \tag{4.10}$$

so that the quantity we seek, the reproducibility error, is simply

$$s_a = \sqrt{s_d^2/2} \tag{4.11}$$

where s_d^2 is computed from the data according to eq. (4.9).

Table 4.2 shows the result of such a test based on duplicate analyses of 47 thin sections of the granites of Milford, N. H., Westerly, R. I., and Barre, Vt. The observed mean ($\bar{x}$, col. 1) was used as an estimate of p in calculating σ (col. 3). (What was the average count length?)

TABLE 4.2. DIFFERENCE TEST FOR REPRODUCIBILITY ERROR OF
POINT COUNTER (DATA FROM CHAYES, 1949)

Mineral	Observed Mean ($\bar{x}$)	Reproducibility Error (observed)	Calculated Binomial Standard Deviation for $p = \bar{x}$
Feldspar and muscovite	65.8	1.22	1.27
Quartz	26.4	0.85	1.19
Biotite	6.6	0.56	0.67
Accessories	1.1	0.33	0.27

It is evident that the binomial standard deviation is a good approximation of that actually observed, and considering the rather limited interest which attaches to reproducibility error as such—once a method is established— it is rather doubtful that a better is needed. Only one of the observed values exceeds the theoretical and two are appreciably smaller.

TABLE 4.3.   OBSERVED MEANS ($\bar{x}$) AND STANDARD DEVIATIONS (s)
FOR DATA OF TABLE 25, FAIRBAIRN ET AL. (1951)[a]

Mineral	$\bar{x}$	s	$\sigma(p = \bar{x}, n = 1502)$
Quartz	27.6	1.28	1.15
Potash feldspar	35.4	1.45	1.23
Plagioclase	31.4	1.40	1.20
Biotite	3.2	0.56	0.45
Muscovite	1.3	0.38	0.29

[a] The third column shows the binomial standard deviation, σ, for $p = \bar{x}, n = 1502$.

Further evidence about counting error is contained in an experiment designed to check the homogeneity of a 6-foot strip of granite. (For a full description of the work see Fairbairn et al., 1951, part 5.) Analyses of

16 thin sections cut at alternate 4- and 6-inch intervals lead to the results posted in Table 4.3.   Each of the five observed values is larger than the theoretical estimate, but in each case the excess is very small.   The situation is one in which such an excess would be expected, for the observed standard deviation includes both counting error and real variation among the thin sections.   In its original context, Table 4.3 was used as evidence that the variability of the rock was very slight.   In conjunction with Table 4.2, however, it is a further indication that the counting or reproducibility error does not differ much from binomial expectation.

All the work so far discussed was done by the same analyst.   A more realistic test, in which five analysts were used, is described in the next chapter.

5

The reproducibility
of thin-section analyses: II_____

In some fields of inquiry, notably in the more "exact" sciences, technical difficulties are very great, and we must often be content with the knowledge that the individual responsible for certain measurements has developed suitable facility. It is neither necessary nor possible, for instance, for every chemist who uses an atomic weight to be able to determine it. It is enough that he knows the best value found by competent specialists working with adequate equipment.

Although the results yielded by a well-established and widely practiced technique of modal analysis might soon obtain this type of currency among non-petrographic geologists, it is clear that the petrographer himself can never so regard them. Modal analysis is of importance in petrography as a technique by which *any* interested petrographer can obtain his own estimates of volume composition. We rarely have need for extraordinarily precise results, but if we can arrange to obtain large numbers of reasonably precise ones there is an excellent chance that we may be able to move descriptive petrography away from the dead center at which it has rested so quietly for half a century.

The burden of analytical work this will require is so large, however, that there is no point undertaking it unless we can be assured of the comparability of results obtained by various petrographers, and this does not seem to prove out in many practical instances. On the whole, however, the data are few and scattered, and the techniques by which they were obtained are variable and poorly described. The problem is of sufficient importance to warrant a careful review of the one fairly adequate test which has been described in print.

In this test five of the thin sections used in the work described at the close of chapter 4 were analyzed by each of five members of the Geology Department of the Massachusetts Institute of Technology. The analysts

TABLE 5.1. INDIVIDUAL RESULTS, SECOND MIT TEST, VOLUME PERCENTAGE
(FROM CHAYES AND FAIRBAIRN, 1953)

Analyst	Slide	Mineral						
		Quartz	Micro-cline	Plagio-clase	Biotite	Muscovite	Opaques	Non-Opaques
I	A	24.7	35.6	33.3	3.3	2.0	0.6	0.6
	B	26.8	35.7	32.6	3.5	0.4	0.6	0.4
	C	28.0	34.2	32.1	3.4	1.1	0.7	0.4
	D	27.8	35.0	31.5	3.3	1.0	0.9	0.5
	E	26.6	34.5	33.6	3.0	1.4	0.6	0.3
	$\bar{x}$	26.8	35.0	32.6	3.3	1.2	0.7	0.4
II	A	27.3	35.5	32.1	2.5	1.5	0.8	0.3
	B	27.3	35.4	31.7	3.4	1.4	0.6	0.1
	C	28.0	35.3	31.1	2.8	1.4	0.8	0.5
	D	30.1	33.8	31.5	2.6	0.9	0.7	0.2
	E	28.7	35.2	31.4	2.6	1.3	0.6	0.2
	$\bar{x}$	28.3	35.0	31.6	2.8	1.3	0.7	0.3
III	A	25.8	36.0	33.5	2.9	0.8	0.7	0.3
	B	25.5	33.9	33.7	4.9	0.8	1.0	0.1
	C	26.1	37.8	30.7	3.4	1.1	0.7	0.3
	D	26.2	36.0	29.5	5.7	1.3	1.1	0.1
	E	27.8	34.7	32.4	3.6	0.7	0.8	0.2
	$\bar{x}$	26.3	35.7	32.0	4.1	0.9	0.9	0.2
IV	A	26.4	36.2	32.7	2.1	1.1	0.8	0.6
	B	26.6	36.3	31.9	3.2	0.8	0.6	0.7
	C	28.1	36.4	30.6	2.4	1.0	1.0	0.6
	D	27.1	35.9	31.6	2.7	0.9	1.1	0.6
	E	28.0	34.6	32.2	3.0	1.0	0.8	0.4
	$\bar{x}$	27.2	35.9	31.8	2.7	1.0	0.9	0.6
V	A	25.2	34.1	34.9	2.6	1.8	0.7	0.6
	B	28.6	34.5	31.6	2.7	1.6	0.6	0.4
	C	28.3	33.0	32.8	3.7	1.0	0.7	0.4
	D	26.3	36.1	32.3	2.9	1.1	0.8	0.5
	E	28.6	34.6	31.9	2.7	1.2	0.5	0.5
	$\bar{x}$	27.4	34.5	32.7	2.9	1.3	0.7	0.5
Grand average		27.2	35.2	32.1	3.2	1.1	0.8	0.4

were competent petrographers. All had done modal analyses in the course of other work, but only one had had previous experience with the point-counting technique. After a short period of instruction and practice, each operator ran the slides in a predetermined random order. A number of months later the entire experiment was repeated, with the results shown in Table 5.1.

When this work was first described no geometrical demonstration of the validity of modal analysis was available, and most of the published modes obtained by point-counting were the work of a single analyst. There was thus no a priori reason to assume either that the slides were consistent samples of the rock or that different analysts working on the same slide were in fact estimating the same (parent) quantities. The statistical treatment necessarily centered on the slide and operator means. On the assumption of sufficient homogeneity of subgroup variance, differences among operators and slides may be evaluated by the usual variance analysis. Such an analysis (see Chayes and Fairbairn, 1953, Table 4B) fails to establish any significant differences among the slides but indicates that for biotite and also for transparent accessories the operators are not in fact estimating the same means. A reasonable explanation of this particular difficulty is offered in the next chapter.

Extraction from the total sum of squares of contributions arising from sections and operators leaves a residue designated as experimental or analytical error. On the assumption that operator and section differences are in fact eliminated by the calculations, the nature of the remaining error is very simple; it can only be the random error which would attach to the work if it had all been done by one man on a single thin section. This is, of course, the reproducibility error, and according to the argument of chapter 4 it ought to be essentially binomial. Table 5.2 shows that this is very nearly the case. Each entry in the row headed Observed error is the square root of the appropriate error mean square calculated from Table 5.1; each entry in the row headed Expected error is calculated from eq. (4.7) with the Grand average of Table 5.1 as an estimate of p. (What was the average count length of the MIT analyses?)

TABLE 5.2. OBSERVED AND EXPECTED REPRODUCIBILITY ERROR
IN THE SECOND MIT TEST

Mineral	Quartz	Micro-cline	Plagio-clase	Biotite	Muscovite	Opaque	Non-Opaque
Observed error	1.0	1.1	0.9	0.6	0.4	0.1	0.1
Expected error	0.89	0.96	0.93	0.35	0.22	0.17	0.12

The work of chapter 1 permits us to consider the data of Table 5.1 in an entirely different light.   It is clear from the introductory discussion—as it was not clear at the time of the MIT test—that the slides, having been taken from the same specimen, are consistent samples of the same parent mean.   Indeed, this would remain true even if the rock were so coarse that the slides differed significantly in composition.   We are also quite sure now that with suitable agreement about identification and tabulation conventions the analysts would necessarily be estimating the same parameters in each slide.   Again, it does not matter that no two analysts get exactly the same result for any particular slide.   They are not merely *recording* the true value; they are *estimating* it.

With this assurance about the homogeneity of the parent means, we may turn at once to an examination of the error variances themselves. What we want is an estimate of the random error attached to the work of each operator.   If we calculate this directly from each man's results for any one mineral we confound random error with real differences between slides.   The latter are no doubt small, but so is the random error.

An alternative procedure, really an elaboration of the difference analysis used in chapter 4, yields estimates of individual operator errors which are free of the effect of slide differences.   The calculation schedule is outlined in Table 5.3 for a subset of the data of Table 5.1, specifically, the quartz values reported by operators I, II, and III.

TABLE 5.3.   QUARTZ DIFFERENCES, BY SLIDES, FOR OPERATORS I, II, AND III, DATA OF TABLE 5.1

Slide	Difference		
	I-II	I-III	II-III
A	−2.6	−1.1	1.5
B	−0.5	1.3	1.8
C	0	1.9	1.9
D	−2.3	1.6	3.9
E	−2.1	−1.2	0.9
$S(X)$	−7.5	2.5	10.0
$S(X^2)$	16.71	10.51	25.12
C	11.25	1.25	20.00
$S(x^2)$	5.46	9.26	5.12
s^2	1.365	2.315	1.28

In the upper half of the table the differences themselves are shown. The calculations at the bottom of the table lead to the variance of the difference (s^2) for each pair of operators. As each difference is calculated for the same slide, whatever differences exist among the slides are immediately eliminated. The correction term C which is subtracted from the total sum of squares of differences is given by $\dfrac{[S(X)]^2}{n} = n\bar{x}^2$,

and $\bar{x}$ is the average difference between operators; the effect of differences between the mean values estimated by each pair of operators is thus removed by the subtraction. The final variance, s^2, obtained by dividing $S(x^2)$ by the number of degrees of freedom (4), therefore contains additive contributions from only two sources, viz., the random error attaching to the work of each operator. We summarize the relation by saying that s_{12}^2 is an estimate of $\sigma_1^2 + \sigma_2^2$, or

$$s_{12}^2 = \sigma_1^2 + \sigma_2^2 \qquad (5.1)$$

where σ denotes true random error and subscripts refer to operators. From the array of difference variances we can readily estimate the individual variances for

$$s_{12}^2 + s_{13}^2 - s_{23}^2 = (\sigma_1^2 + \sigma_2^2) + (\sigma_1^2 + \sigma_3^2) - (\sigma_2^2 + \sigma_3^2) = 2\sigma_1^2$$
$$(5.2)$$

The quantity on the left is tallied from the table and leads at once to an estimate of σ_1, the standard deviation from random error attaching to analyst I's quartz values. By rotating subscripts we can also obtain similar estimates for σ_2 and σ_3. The values reached in this fashion are $\sigma_1 = 1.10$, $\sigma_2 = 0.41$, $\sigma_3 = 1.06$.

The procedure can be generalized for $^nC_2$ sets of pairs, where n is the number of individuals, by breaking the total sum of the difference variances into two parts: A, including all difference variances to which σ_i contributes, and B, including all difference variances which contain no contribution from σ_i. By enumeration it is easily shown that

$$\sigma_i^2 = \frac{A}{n-1} - \frac{B}{(n-1)(n-2)}$$
$$= \frac{1}{(n-1)(n-2)}[(n-2)A - B] \qquad (5.3)[1]$$

the latter form being a little more convenient for computation.

For the full data of Table 5.1 we have five analysts; hence there will be $^5C_2$ or 10 sets of difference variances, and the individual analyst error

---

[1] The relation may also be written $(n-1)!\sigma_i^2 = (n-2)!A - (n-3)!B$, which seems a little more elegant.

variances will be estimated from

$$\sigma_i^2 = \frac{1}{4 \cdot 3}[3A - B]$$

where A is the sum of the four difference variances containing σ_i^2 and B is the sum of the six from which it is absent.   Proceeding in this fashion with the first four columns of Table 5.1, we reach the estimates shown in Table 5.4.   Entries in the last three columns of Table 5.1 are conveniently small; the interested reader may wish to use them in practice calculations.

TABLE 5.4.   ESTIMATED STANDARD DEVIATIONS FOR
RANDOM ERROR OF ANALYSTS, BY MINERAL

Analyst	Mineral			
	Quartz	Microcline	Plagioclase	Biotite
I	0.83	1.29	0.27	0.22
II	1.08	0.46	0.56	0.14
III	0.96	1.47	1.39	1.07
IV	0.47	0.24	0.34	0.25
V	1.30	1.40	1.23	0.60
Average	0.93	0.97	0.76	0.46
Expected (binomial)	0.89	0.96	0.93	0.35

The *average* random error for each mineral is again quite close to binomial expectation, and for each of the major minerals it is less than the value given by conventional variance analysis (compare the row headed Average of Table 5.4 with the row headed Observed error of Table 5.2).   There seems to be no approved method for assigning degrees of freedom to the new estimates, so that exact tests of them are not possible,[2]

[2] Clearly we do not obtain a degree of freedom for each paired difference; if we are given the four involving any one analyst we can immediately calculate (additively) the remaining six connecting the other four analysts.   As only 25 determinations have been made for each mineral this is the maximum number of degrees of freedom available.   In the ordinary analysis of variance we lose 1 to the grand mean, 4 to the slides, 4 to the analysts, and retain 16 for the over-all estimate of random error.   In theory the latter are contributed uniformly, so that, in a sense, each analyst contributes 3.2 of them.   In the difference calculation no grand mean is calculated, and no comparisons affected by differences between slides are made, so that, presumably, 5 degrees of freedom are available for each individual estimate.   This is not much of a gain.   The real advantage of the method, however, is not that it leads to a particularly powerful estimate but that it leads to *an* estimate of the random error of each analyst without assuming that this error is the same for all analysts.   The assignment of degrees of freedom to the *average* values of Table 5.4 is a troublesome matter.   The five individual estimates are scarcely independent yet their dependence is difficult to specify.   Fortunately, the close agreement between relevant entries in the last two rows of the table makes discussion of this point unnecessary.

but there is nothing to prevent our examining Table 5.4 as closely as we wish. The main point of the argument is made by the last two rows of the table. It is hard to see why the average error is so close to binomial expectation unless a very large part of the error variance is in fact binomial. In detail, however, there is a suggestion that random error is not the same for all analysts. Between them, analysts III and V are responsible for seven of the eight largest entries in the table. Analyst IV's random error, on the other hand, seems very low throughout. It is to be remembered however, that large deviations in one mineral must be reflected in others. In theory, the presence of a few per cent of minerals other than quartz and feldspar provides a kind of cushion against a one-to-one compensation of large deviations in the major minerals. In practice, this is probably not very effective in small samples; more precisely, from the five analyses shown for each analyst in Table 5.1, it is impossible to tell whether the cushion is working.

The question of whether the reproducibility error is strictly binomial will require additional discussion in a later chapter. As Table 5.4 indicates, however, its interest is largely academic. With a reasonable amount of practice, any competent petrographer ought to be able to hold his random counting error to approximately a binomial expectation. As we shall see, there is some evidence that an analyst with long experience can beat this expectation by a small margin. The evidence is not conclusive, and the margin of superiority, if real, is very small.

6

Identification and
tabulation conventions

The errors with which we have so far been concerned are not in any sense mistakes. The statistical error can be reduced but never altogether avoided; it is a part of the properly performed measuring process. The non-statistical mistake, on the other hand, can be avoided but not reduced; we either make it or we do not. Except for gross blunders such as inadvertent repetition of traverse lines or accidental recording faults, the mistakes of modal analysis consist almost entirely of misidentification. Elimination of such mistakes is essentially non-statistical, but it is important to realize that a valid statistical examination of error presupposes their absence. The competent modal analyst is first of all a competent petrographer. Resistance of petrographers to statistical examination of their work sometimes seems to be based on the feeling that it is essentially an indictment of their competence. Nothing could be further from the truth. The statistician's first assumption, the one from which he operates most easily and efficiently, and which he abandons only under extreme duress, is just that the petrographer does *not* make mistakes.

Between the clearly recognizable non-statistical mistake and the clearly recognizable random error extends a troublesome middle ground occupied by mistake-like errors and error-like mistakes. The definition and discussion of these phenomena are only slightly less difficult than their experimental treatment. Provisionally, at least, we may group them in two broad classes, those which are essentially identification faults and those which arise from instability in or lack of agreement about tabulation conventions.

1. THE IDENTIFICATION FAULT

This is perhaps best described as an error-like mistake. The well-trained eye is a sensitive instrument, and many of the discriminations we

51

make as a matter of course in qualitative petrography are extraordinarily subtle. Given all the time needed and freedom to apply all the resources of the petrographic microscope, most competent petrographers would be able to distinguish properly, for instance, between most grains of potash-feldspar and albite lying side by side. When a long succession of such grains is drawn across the field of vision at a fairly rapid rate, however, there is no time to apply all the tests. Some of the identifications are inevitably based on properties, as, for instance, shape, or degree of alteration, which are neither specific to nor necessarily present in all grains of a particular species. And, as everyone who has tried this will confess, many are just plain guesses. To an extent which will vary with analysts, rocks, and even lighting, these identifications will be wrong. Strictly speaking, each such identification fault is a mistake—by careful examination most of them could be avoided—but as doubtful grains are classified now one way and now another, the over-all effect is very likely to be some bias in the estimate of both constituents, and there will almost certainly be an enlargement of the precision error of both estimates.

If numerous slides are run in common by two analysts, significant differences in mean values are rather easily detected, but there may be no way of deciding which analyst is estimating the true value and the safest assumption will usually be that neither is doing so.

The contribution of the identification fault to the error variance, on the other hand, may often escape detection. If the work has been done by point counter we may argue that any excess of reproducibility error over binomial expectation is cause for alarm. Unless the experimental design is such as to permit separate estimates of precision error for each analyst, however, there is nothing we can do but be alarmed. In fact, even our ability to detect the difficulty exists only if the work has been planned and at least partly programmed with this in mind. If we are to place any credence in comparisons of different rocks based on modes obtained by different analysts—the kind of comparison invited or implied, for instance, by every tabulation of data culled from the journal literature—we must be reasonably sure that identification faults are not serious in the work of *any* analyst involved.

The solution to the problem created by identification faults is very simple. Minerals should be distinguished from each other in quantitative modal analysis only when they can be easily, clearly, and rapidly identified. This is the principal justification for staining potash feldspar in slides of granitic rocks. In a very large preponderance of cases the two types of feldspar can be distinguished from each other without any etch or stain, but the distinction is commonly difficult and slow, and unless every resource of the microscope is brought into play it is sometimes indecisive. The characteristic bright yellow of microcline in a well-stained granite slide, on the other hand, is clear and unmistakable. In an unstained slide the results for microcline and plagioclase will be subject to a large identification fault; in a well-stained slide the identification fault for this particular pair of minerals will be negligible.

Occasionally even a cautious petrographer may feel tempted to run analyses whose results he knows or suspects will be subject to a serious identification fault. There are, of course, situations in which this would be justifiable, though interpretation of the results is not likely to be wholly satisfactory. A systematic composition trend, for instance, may be strong enough to make itself felt even in relation to an error variance enlarged by identification faults. Spurious trends may also arise because of identification faults, however, and the fact that a series of analyses characterized by a large identification fault fails to reveal a trend is not reliable evidence that the trend does not exist.

Even when analyses containing large identification faults are either unavoidable or decidedly useful, there is no assurance that they provide unbiased estimates of true composition. Such analyses can be unbiased only if the first of the two minerals involved in the fault is mistaken for the second as often as the second is mistaken for the first. And how can we ever be sure of this? Indeed, there seems every reason to suppose that an exact compensation of this sort will be very rare; modal analyses subject to an identification fault will usually be biased with regard to the minerals involved in the fault, but from such analyses themselves we shall be unable to estimate the bias, or even to detect it.

2. TABULATION CONVENTIONS

Even when identifications are clear, uncertainty or lack of agreement about tabulation conventions may cause trouble. In a medium- or coarse-grained two-feldspar granite, for instance, the potash feldspar will almost certainly be somewhat perthitic. Is the albite member of the perthite to be tallied with the potash feldspar or with the plagioclase? (It can of course be tallied separately, but generally this merely defers the decision, for it is rarely present in sufficient amount to be more than a nuisance in the posting of the final result.) Most of the unstained feldspar will usually be sharply tabular and somewhat blocky in outline. It is likely to show the same zoning as plagioclase not included in potash feldspar, and it will almost certainly be altered in the same fashion. Perthitic albite, on the other hand, usually forms strings, films, or blebs much smaller than the tablets of included plagioclase, and is commonly unaltered. In almost any thin section, however, there will be some scraps of unstained feldspar enclosed in microcline which cannot be clearly assigned to either class. Different analysts may not agree about tabulation of these doubtful cases—indeed, they may not even agree that a particular grain is a doubtful case—and over a long period of time the tabulation conventions adopted by a single analyst may shift without his knowledge. In the analysis of most two-feldspar granite this is fortunately a minor problem. When total plagioclase is very low, however, as in the one-feldspar granites, it may be extremely troublesome; work on such rocks ought to be planned to permit considerable interanalyst comparison.

Whether this particular question is regarded as a problem in identification or tabulation is to some extent a matter of taste. A somewhat similar problem which is clearly concerned with tabulation rather than identification arises in connection with the treatment of chlorite forming as an alteration of biotite in granitic rocks. In such rocks biotite entirely free of chlorite is very rare, but in fresh specimens the total amount of chlorite is invariably small. Usually nothing at all is gained by recording it separately, and it is included either with biotite or as a member of the non-opaque accessories. An instructive example of confusion on this score is provided by the MIT precision test described in the preceding chapter. It has already been mentioned that conventional variance analysis of Table 5.1 indicates that there are significant differences between analyst means for biotite and also for non-opaque accessories. It is time now to point out that this difference is established against an observed error variance whose square root (0.571) is 60 per cent larger than the expected binomial value (0.35). Table 5.1 shows that analyst III is primarily responsible for the differences in the mean values; his is by far the highest biotite average, 4.1 per cent as compared to 2.9 for the others. It does not necessarily follow that he is responsible for the excess of observed over expected error variance, but in fact he does seem to have contributed most of it. The average standard deviation for the other four analysts, calculated according to eq. (5.3), is 0.30 as compared to 0.46 for the full array and an expected value of 0.35 (see Table 5.4).

Analyst III not only reports the highest average value for biotite; his is also the lowest value for non-opaque accessories. In this respect, however, he reflects what seems to be a general tendency. Assigning integral ranks in order of increasing size of average values shown in Table 5.1, we have, for all five analysts,

Analyst	Biotite	Non-Opaques	Σ
I	4	3	7
II	2	2	4
III	5	1	6
IV	1	5	6
V	3	4	7

Although the data are insufficient for an exact test, the rank sums do suggest that the average value for non-opaques varies inversely with the average value for biotite.   The obvious explanation of this effect is a lack of standardization with regard to the tabulation of chlorite.   Probably most of the difficulty represents constant differences among the operators, each man differing somewhat from the others in the proportion of chlorite he regards as completely dissociated from biotite.   The further possibility that individual operator conventions shifted somewhat during the test cannot be excluded.

All this suggests a somewhat different approach to the data.   By far the most abundant of the minerals tallied under Non-Opaque is chlorite, and the distinction between Biotite and Non-Opaque is evidently unsatisfactory for the rather special purpose we have in mind.   It thus seems reasonable to abandon this distinction.   For the sum Biotite + Non-Opaques variance analysis of Table 5.1 fails to indicate significant differences between analysts.   Individual analyst standard deviations for the sum Biotite + Non-Opaques, calculated according to eq. (5.3), vary from 0.05 for analyst IV to 0.83 for analyst I.   The average for the five analysts, however. is 0.32 as compared to an expected (binomial) counting error of 0.36.

In the terms in which we ordinarily think of modal analysis the differences under discussion are small. The grand average for Biotite in Table 5.1 is 3.2 per cent, that for the sum Biotite + Non-Opaques is only 3.6 per cent; petrographic problems which can be solved by determining that an observed difference of 0.4 per cent is either significant or fortuitous are very rare. Our concern here, however, is not with mean values but with error, and the effect of minor identification or tabulation difficulties on error variance can easily be disastrous.   In the numerical example used, for instance, the mean value for the sum of Biotite + Non-Opaques is only 12.5 per cent more than that for biotite alone, but inclusion of non-opaques with biotite very nearly halves the average analyst variance.

In sum, identification faults and unstable or inadequately standardized tabulation conventions tend to bias mean values, to increase apparent negative correlations between the minerals or mineral groups concerned, and to inflate analytical error.   Their influence on covariance and variance is likely to be much more important than their effect on mean values. The enlargement of error is itself sufficiently serious, for, other things being equal, the strength and utility of any small sample statistical test are controlled by the size of the error variance.   Far more critical, however, is the *way* in which identification faults and tabulation conventions enlarge the error variance.   Their effects will almost certainly differ widely from analyst to analyst so that the assumption of homogeneous subgroup variances, an assumption upon which the validity of much statistical testing hinges, may easily be vitiated. In any experimental program sufficiently extensive to require the services of several analysts or the work of one analyst over a considerable period of time, identification problems and tabulation conventions should be carefully discussed *before* work is begun.

7

A working definition
of analytical error
in modal analysis

Up to this point the discussion has been of a general character. We have seen that measurements made in the usual fashion are consistent estimates of areal proportions, and that the "composition" of an area selected at random is a consistent sample of volumetric proportions. This much of the problem is geometrical rather than geological, and its examination was carried through with no reference to rocks—in fact, without measurements of any sort. The a priori treatment led directly to a theoretical estimate of the reproducibility error attaching to results obtained by point-counting, and we have seen that the reproducibility error observed in three experimental studies is in fact quite close to the theoretical expectation.

Although the experiments were carried out on rocks, actually on rocks of a particular kind, this in no way affects the generality of our findings. In exactly the sense in which the precision of a balance is independent of the object being weighed, the reproducibility of point-counting is independent of the nature of the areas being measured. It makes no difference whether the measurement surface is derived from biological tissues, from metals, from ore minerals or mineral assemblages, or from rocks of any type whatever.

Most of the remainder of this book is concerned with the efficiency of thin sections as samples of hand specimens, an aspect of variation which has so far successfully resisted a priori analysis. It can be described in rather general terms, but the generality of the terms stems largely from their superficiality. In earlier chapters experiment was used largely by way of illustration. We now begin to use it as a guide, for we have no other. The analogy of the chemical balance will perhaps make this distinction a little clearer.

In the operation of weighing we can distinguish at least two sources of error.   One of these is purely instrumental; it expresses the departure from exact agreement that would be observed by an operator reweighing the same object under optimum circumstances.   (We assume that differences in competence among skilled operators are small enough to neglect.) This we call the precision (or precision error) of the *balance*, and it is obviously independent of the object being weighed.   In fact, we may define it as that part of the total variation which *is* independent of the nature of the object being weighed.

The error governing the weighing of a real object can never be less than the precision error of the balance and will almost always be larger. Although it does not affect the precision error of the balance, the nature of the object being weighed does influence the weighing error, and much time and effort are expended in holding this influence to a minimum. The precision error of the balance, which must be experimentally determined, is analogous to the reproducibility of point-counting, which we have developed largely on a priori grounds.   In our analogy the hand specimen plays the role of the real object being weighed; the nature of the hand specimen does not influence the reproducibility of results obtained on any particular thin section cut from it but certainly does influence the *analytical error*, which we may now define as *the random error attaching to the analysis as an estimate of the composition of the hand specimen from which the section is cut.*[1]

Like all analogies, this one must not be pushed too far.   The occasion of its failure, however, is rather unexpected.   Although in a relative sense the error of weighing will nearly always be far smaller than the analytical error of modal analysis, the latter is much simpler in structure and correspondingly easier to control.   The balance may be either precise or imprecise, but in itself it is neither accurate nor inaccurate. We cannot begin to think of its accuracy until we provide it with a set of calibrated weights, and of course the calibration will be subject to error. Quite aside from this, the contribution of the objects being weighed to the weighing error is quite likely to introduce some bias.   An object whose dry weight is sought, for instance, no doubt has a dry weight, and no legitimate manipulation can make it weigh less than this.   Operations which are satisfactory by every other experimental standard, however, may fail to remove some small fraction of the water, and letting it sit on the balance pan long enough so that we can weigh it with extreme care may introduce some water into it.

---

[1] In an earlier paper (Chayes, 1950) the reproducibility error described in chapters 4 and 5 is called "analytical" or "experimental."   The usage suggested here seems more reasonable and more practical.

Similarly, objects being brought to "room temperature" in desiccators may sometimes fail to reach that temperature before they are weighed but will not fall below it. The thermal effect on the weighing, and hence on the apparent weight, may thus vary in size but not in sign. In competent analytical work these and many similar effects are no doubt so small as to be negligible. They nevertheless seriously complicate our thinking about the weighing process. In particular, we cannot suppose that the result of the operation of weighing, however often that operation is repeated, necessarily converges on the true weight. This would hold only for a weighing process so refined and hedged about with restrictions as to bear little resemblance to the real thing.

The situation in modal analysis is on the whole quite different. If the intersections of grain contacts with the plane of measurement can be accurately located, the difference between sampling a thin section with points and sampling a hand specimen with thin sections is reflected entirely in the variances governing the two operations. If a single analysis is made of each of, say, n thin sections cut from a hand specimen, the observed scatter will usually be larger than if n analyses are made of one of the thin sections. But in either case each individual analysis is legitimately regarded as a consistent estimate of the same parent parameter, and this parameter is in fact the quantity we seek to estimate, the volumetric composition of the rock. The counting or reproducibility error tells us how wide a bracket we must place about an observed value in order to include, with some given probability, the true value *for the slide*. In the same fashion, the analytical error tells us how wide a bracket we must place about an observed value in order to include, with some given probability, the true value *for the specimen from which the slide has been cut*.

As we have seen, it is possible to construct a simple geometrical model which yields a theoretical counting error very close to that actually observed in point-counting. No such model can be constructed for the analytical error. We shall have to content ourselves with a rather vague description of the factors controlling the size of the analytical error; estimation of its size in any particular kind of rock is a matter for experiment. As the necessary minimum of experimentation has been carried through on only one kind of rock, both the argument and the numerical conclusions in the succeeding pages of this book are of less general import than those already discussed. A rather detailed account of the work on analytical error nevertheless seems worth while, not only because of the abundance and importance of the kind of rock on which it has been performed, but more especially because a somewhat similar program will have to be carried through on a number of rock types before modal analysis can be regarded as an established analytical technique.

Let us suppose for the moment that we could measure exactly the "composition" of each of a number of thin sections cut from a particular hand specimen. If the specimen were very fine-grained, the thin sections would differ little if at all from each other; the contribution of the specimen to the analytical error would thus be virtually nil, and, in the ideal situation we have agreed to imagine, the analytical error as measured by dispersion of results would be practically zero. In real work, of course, we never know the true compositions of the thin sections but are forced to use estimates which are always subject to error. If the thin sections are in fact identical, however, the only non-zero component of the analytical error is just this measurement error, which we have already referred to as counting or reproducibility error. The analytical error may thus never be less than the error of areal measurement, and from the preceding work we have a good idea of the magnitude of this error for measurements made by point-counting.

If we now hold the size of the measurement area on each thin section constant but allow the grain size or coarseness of the specimen to increase, we shall find that even though our individual thin-section analyses are errorless, the results will differ from section to section. The same effect would be obtained if the grain size of the specimen remained fixed but the measurement area per thin section were reduced. In practice, again, the counting error is not zero—in the usual arrangement it will be about 1 per cent for major constituents—and the analytical error will exceed it by an amount which reflects the magnitude of the variation observed in our ideal experiment. As the specimen effect and the counting error are independent, the analytical error will be given by

$$\sigma_a = \sqrt{\sigma_c^2 + \sigma_s^2}$$

where σ_a is the analytical error, σ_c is the counting error, and σ_s^2 is the specimen variance.

That the same effect may be produced by enlarging the grain size or reducing the measurement area indicates that the controlling factor is the relation between the two rather than either one separately. What matters is not the size of the grains or the size of the measurement area, but *the number of grain sections per measurement area*. If the distribution of grains in the rock were random to the extent that the identity of a particular grain was independent of the identity of its nearer neighbors, analytical error would be inversely proportional to the square root of the grain frequency per unit area.

This grossly oversimplified discussion suggests that our first order of business should be concerned with estimating the number of grains per unit area, and in some rocks this stratagem might be successful. In the particular rocks chosen for study, however, the matter proves to be far more complex than this. In succeeding chapters we shall first illustrate the effect of grain number without really counting the number of grains, and next develop a measure of coarseness without defining, in any strict sense, what we mean by grain or grain size. This approach is unavoidable because in the granitic fabric it has so far proved impossible to specify, in any usable fashion, what is meant by a single grain.

8

Effect of grain size and area of measurement on analytical error_____

1. THE DIFFICULTY OF MEASURING GRAIN SIZE

Analytical error stands midway between the type of variation characteristic of a measuring process and the type of variation characteristic of assemblages of the objects being measured. In our case the process is the estimation of areas by point-counting, and the assemblage of objects may consist either of specimens collected from a geologically defined rock mass, or of petrographically (taxonomically) similar specimens collected from different masses. The crucial importance of analytical error is evident; a small analytical error creates and a large analytical error precludes the possibility of detecting or measuring small differences. The differences in which we are interested may be compared to pebbles we are attempting to rake, the analytical error to the distance between the tines of the rake.

In the preceding chapter we defined analytical error as the random error attaching to the analysis as an estimate of the composition of the *hand specimen* from which the section is cut, and we indicated that analytical error—unlike reproducibility error—may differ from specimen to specimen in response to changes in the frequency of grain sections per measurement area. In conventional petrographic jargon the effect in question is said to be attributable to "grain size" and its importance has long been appreciated. Rosiwal, for instance, remarks that "Es ist leicht einzusehen, dass der Genauigkeitsgrad ... umgekehrt proportional der Korngross des Gesteines sein muss," and Richardson clearly understood that the effect of coarseness of grain was to render the results of thin-section analysis ". . . highly susceptible to the vagaries of sampling." Richardson also realized that the way to control and reduce extraneous variation of this sort was by replication.

Whether we prefer to regard the controlling factor as "grain size" itself, or as the relative frequency of grain sections per measurement area, the next step would appear to be obvious. In the first case we ought to measure "grain size"; in the second we ought to estimate the numbers of grain sections per unit area. If we could do one of these things we could do the other. In the rocks with which the remainder of this book is concerned—the two-feldspar granites—it has so far proved impossible to do either with suitable precision. Of course, every petrographer makes an estimate of "grain size" in the course of everyday field work. Fortunately, most of us never make any use of these estimates. Even the occasional petrographer who, like Richardson, has clearly appreciated the connection between grain size and analytical error, has nevertheless refrained from any systematic attempt to use his measurements as a guide to the amount of replication required per specimen in modal analysis.

The general lack of success in measuring grain size in thin section—and the as yet complete failure of attempts to estimate relative frequency of grain sections per unit area—is largely a consequence of the complexity of the granitic fabric. In a fabric consisting of grains of simple outline either type of measurement would probably be relatively simple, and the relation connecting them might even be fairly tractable. Where most grain boundaries are extremely complex, intricate marginal intergrowths are the rule rather than the exception, and large "individuals" often prove to be aggregates, it is usually difficult to say just what is meant by *a* grain. If this test can be passed, it is still necessary to be able to specify *shape* before much meaning can be attached to size, however measured.[1] It would be very difficult to say just what, if anything, we mean by the shape of a strongly poikilitic or skeletal crystal of microcline, for instance. Yet if we want to define some usable parameter of size—maximum length, average maximum length, etc.—it must be some dimension, or the average of some group of dimensions, of a geometrically specified shape. In the granitic fabric we are rarely able to provide an adequate specification of shape.

It might seem that an actual tally of the numbers of grain sections could easily be made, however complex the outlines of the sections. The considerations which make size measurements difficult and virtually uninterpretable, however, exert a similar effect on number counts. In sum, the counting or measuring of grain sections of major minerals in the granitic fabric is usually a rather impractical procedure. The physical interpretation to be attached to the results is dubious at best—indeed, it is often questionable whether there is one—and their precision ordinarily leaves much to be desired. We usually learn no more from measurements

[1] Possibly in the absence of re-entrants this would not be essential. In connection with the granitic fabric the possibility is hardly worth exploring.

or counts of this type than we do from snap judgments based on casual hand-specimen inspection.   And this is not enough.

For present purposes we thus require some way of characterizing the effect of coarseness on dispersion without actually measuring or counting the grain sections.   If we insist on regarding grain size in the conventional manner this is a nearly insoluble problem.   Our interest, however, is not at all in grain size as such.   Rather, we are concerned with the effect of relative frequency (or abundance) of grain sections on analytical error. This can be studied either by varying the measurement area or by varying the coarseness of the material being analyzed, for it is obvious that the average abundance of grain sections will vary directly with the size of the measurement area and inversely with the coarseness of the rock.

Now although we may not be able to characterize grain size metrically, we can easily grade hand specimens for coarseness.   If we use specimens which differ markedly enough in coarseness we shall all agree about the *order* of coarseness of the specimens, though no two observers may agree about the "distance" between adjacent specimens.   A series of analyses carried out with thin sections of some fixed area will yield a different variance for each specimen.   If the count length is fixed and the specimens are of about the same bulk composition, significant differences in dispersion from specimen to specimen will be primarily controlled by differences in coarseness.   We thus obtain a series of direct comparisons, but as we have no measure of the coarseness of the specimens we cannot characterize the effect quantitatively.   In fact, our independent parameter, coarseness, is not a variable but an attribute.

Alternatively, we may standardize on coarseness and count length, and vary measurement area.   In this case the independent parameter, area of measurement, is a true variable, and we may thus find, *for each specimen*, an empirical relation between it and analytical error.   Finally, we may compare the empirical function found for one specimen with that found for another of different coarseness; so long as coarseness is an attribute rather than a variable, however, a tabular or graphical comparison of the various regression curves is about as far as the analysis can be carried.

2. EXPERIMENTAL PROCEDURE AND DATA

A study of the sort suggested above has been carried through with four area sizes on each of three hand specimens, the latter purposely selected because of obvious differences in coarseness.   The specimens used were:

(*a*) A small block from the end of the six-foot strip from the Smith quarry, Westerly, R. I., used as one of the standards in the chemical survey described in U.S. Geological Survey Bull. 980 (Fairbairn et al., 1951).

(*b*) A specimen from a small working near Hall's Quarry Village, Mt. Desert, Me.

(*c*) A specimen from the Carnsew quarry, in the Carnmenellis granite, not far from the town of Penryn, Cornwall, England.

Most of the granites which form medium-sized plutons are of a coarseness comparable to the quarry granites of Mt. Desert. Granites as fine as this particular specimen of Westerly rarely form independent masses of any size. Granites as coarse as Carnmenellis are rarely analyzed by thin section.

As far as major minerals are concerned, all three of the specimens are perfectly ordinary two-feldspar granites. Biotite is the only dark mineral of any importance in Westerly and Mt. Desert; it is rather extensively chloritized in the former, very fresh in the latter, and amounts to about 5 per cent by volume of each. The color index of Carnmenellis is a little over 14, and the specimen contains in abundance all the mineralogical delicacies for which the granites of Cornwall and Devon are famous.

From each specimen twenty thin sections were cut, each containing a measurement area 24 × 40 mm. On ten of the sections of each specimen this area was subdivided into three, one 4 × 40 mm., another 8 × 40 mm., and the third 12 × 40 mm. The other ten thin sections of each specimen were used without subdivision. From each specimen there were thus available for analysis suites of ten areas at each of four sizes, the area sizes being in the ratio 1 : 2 : 3 : 6. The smallest area—160 mm.² or about ¼ in.²—is certainly smaller than is common nowadays in routine modal analysis. The largest area is 960 mm.² or a little over 1½ in.², probably somewhat larger than those most petrographers use. The ratio 1 : 2 : 3 : 6 was chosen because a symmetrical and not strongly anisotropic grid containing the same number of points could be laid out in each area, so that the counting error would be the same for all areas. The actual count length was only 660, rather less than half that used in regular analytical work, but this was the largest that could be arranged. Results of the analyses are summarized in Table 8.1.

3. A Statistical Description of Table 8.1

From the preceding discussion, particularly that of section 1, it is pretty obvious that we shall have to be content with a rather crude empirical reduction of the data. Even without that discussion, however, the character of the data and of our interest in them makes it essential to avoid over-refinements. In most elementary statistical work of this sort our only interest in the standard deviation is as a measure of variation in the mean. In the present case we are interested in the standard deviations themselves, and the means are posted only to indicate that: (*a*) they agree very well for different measurement areas of the same specimen, and (b) all of them are in the region in which, as far as reproducibility error and binomial sampling generally are concerned, the standard deviation is rather insensitive to shifts in mean value. For $n = 660$, $\sigma = 1.60$ for the smallest $\bar{x}$ in the table and 1.89 for the largest.

TABLE 8.1. SUMMARY OF ANALYTICAL DATA[a]

Specimen	Mineral	A							
		160 mm.^{2}		320 mm.^{2}		480 mm.^{2}		960 mm.^{2}	
		$\bar{x}$	s	$\bar{x}$	s	$\bar{x}$	s	$\bar{x}$	s
Westerly	Quartz	26.5	1.78	27.6	2.05	27.0	1.52	27.3	1.57
	K-spar	37.7	2.05	37.0	2.02	36.3	1.40	37.4	1.64
	Plagioclase	30.5	1.92	30.4	1.90	31.4	1.39	30.5	1.27
	$\sqrt{\bar{V}_p}$		1.92		1.99		1.44		1.50
Mt. Desert	Quartz	34.9	3.63	36.7	2.94	33.7	2.76	33.5	1.68
	K-spar	34.9	3.60	35.1	2.49	37.0	4.18	36.5	2.70
	Plagioclase	27.0	3.65	25.4	2.42	26.6	3.05	26.7	2.67
	$\sqrt{\bar{V}_p}$		3.62		2.62		3.39		2.40
Carnmen-	Quartz	31.8	10.66	33.0	6.20	34.3	6.46	31.8	5.21
ellis	K-spar	28.9	12.29	29.5	5.18	25.2	5.52	29.9	4.19
	Plagioclase	25.9	6.35	24.6	2.80	26.6	2.67	25.8	2.65
	$\sqrt{\bar{V}_p}$		10.07		4.94		5.14		4.16

[a] $\bar{x}$, average; s, standard deviation; A, area of measurement.

Our interest in the standard deviation as such causes trouble because the estimate of it obtained from a small sample is very poor. The standard deviation estimated for each mineral-area combination is subject to a very large uncertainty. Each being based on only ten observations, the 0.90 confidence belt extends from $0.7293s$ to $1.645s$, where s is the observed value. An observed value of 2.5, for instance, merely signifies a 0.90 probability that the true value lies somewhere between 1.8 and 4.1. The uncertainty attached to any one observed value is thus very much larger than the total range of σ implied by variation in $\bar{x}$. As if this were not bad enough, the width of the confidence band is itself a function of s; the larger s, the broader the band within which there is any particular probability of finding the true value. (Stated in another way, the larger the observed s, the less likely is it that a band of some particular width about s will include σ.)

A second complication arises from the fact that we have more data than we can conveniently use.   Our primary objective is to study the relation between s and A in each of three rocks, but we have three observations of s for each A.   These are admittedly for different minerals, but the means for the three minerals are usually not very different.   We have already noted that, from the point of view of any binomial sampling situation, the differences in means are too small to exert much influence on the standard deviations.

It would obviously be a great convenience to average the three standard deviations recorded for each area-rock combination, and, as long as the sensitivity of variance to mean was no greater in the actual sampling situation than in the theoretical binomial one, there would appear to be no critical objection to such a procedure on this score.   Averaging does of course obscure or eliminate differences in variability among the different minerals.   Such differences certainly do exist, particularly between minerals of very different habit or coarseness, but they are probably not nearly as important as might be expected, since the variances, particularly if large, are not truly independent.

To make this a little clearer let us imagine a rock consisting entirely of phenocrysts of microcline set in a matrix of very fine oligoclase and quartz. A small measurement area may give an excellent estimate of the ratio oligoclase/quartz, but will certainly give a poor one of the amount of microcline in the rock.   Now an underestimate of microcline necessarily leads to an overestimate of quartz + oligoclase, and an overestimate of microcline to an underestimate of quartz + oligoclase.   Thus a small measurement area must give a poor estimate of the amount of quartz or oligoclase in the rock *because* it gives a poor estimate of the amount of microcline.   The effects will not be identical, of course—they will probably be proportional to mean values—but generally it seems most unlikely that large *differences* in variance will arise from differences in habit or coarseness.   Rather, the variance effect arising from the coarseness or unique habit of some constituent is probably distributed over all the constituents of the rock.

In sum, there seems to be no compelling argument against averaging the s values in each box of Table 8.1.   The next question is how the averaging should be carried through.   Whenever there is any choice, statisticians evidently prefer to operate with the mean square rather than the root mean square.   The numerical difference between the average standard deviation and the square root of the average variance is very small over most of the table, and appreciable only in Carnmenellis.

The square root of the average precision variance has been used in all subsequent calculations; it is indicated by $\sqrt{\bar{V}_p}$ in Table 8.1 and elsewhere in the paper. $\sqrt{\bar{V}}$ is a somewhat more conservative measure of precision than $\bar{s}$, since $\sqrt{\bar{V}} \geqslant \bar{s}$.

In this fashion we reduce the data of Table 8.1 to manageable dimensions; with a single estimate of error for each rock-area combination, we can begin to examine the relation between area of measurement and error in each rock.   It is also reasonable to suppose that the average error variance is itself subject to smaller error than the individual values, though we have no way of knowing whether the improvement is more or less than would be expected from a doubling of the degrees of freedom.

With only four points for each rock, it is obvious that we shall have to be satisfied with a linear approximation of the relation between A and $\sqrt{\bar{V}_p}$.   But shall we use the raw data or transform to some other scale before fitting the curves?

We have already noted that $\sqrt{\bar{V}_p}$ contains contributions from two sources, the counting error, which has been fixed by standardizing the count length, and sampling variation.   We may thus write

$$E(\bar{V}_p) = k_1 + \sigma_s^2 \qquad (8.1)$$

where k is the counting variance and σ_s^2 the sampling variance.   Further, we may regard each measurement area as the sum of a large number of very small (unit) areas, so that the number of these present in the different measurement areas are in the ratios of the areas to each other.   A certain parent sampling variance, σ_μ^2, being associated with the unit area at each coarseness (i.e., in each of the three hand specimens), we have that $\sigma_s^2 = (k_2\sigma_\mu^2)/A$ so that eq. (8.1) may be written

$$E(\bar{V}_p) = k_1 + \frac{k_2\sigma_\mu^2}{A} \qquad (8.2)$$

From eq. (8.2) it is clear that the basic relationship between $E(\bar{V}_p)$ and A is not linear, so that a linear approximation carried through on the experimental results is likely to be pretty poor.   If k_1 is small in relation to σ_s^2, however, the parent relation will be essentially linear if the raw values are transformed to logs.   If k_1 is small enough to ignore, the relation becomes exactly linear in logs for, since σ_μ is fixed at a particular coarseness, we have for any particular specimen

$$\log E(\bar{V}_p) = \log (k_2k_3) - \log A \qquad (8.3)$$

There is thus a strong indication that the curve fitting should be carried through with the logs of the observed values rather than with the observed values themselves, though we may anticipate trouble where k_1 is large in relation to σ_s^2, as will be true for large areas of fine-grained rocks. Incidentally, since σ_s^2 is non-negative, eq. (8.1) shows that $E(\bar{V}_p) \geqslant k_1$; the counting error sets a lower limit to the analytical error.

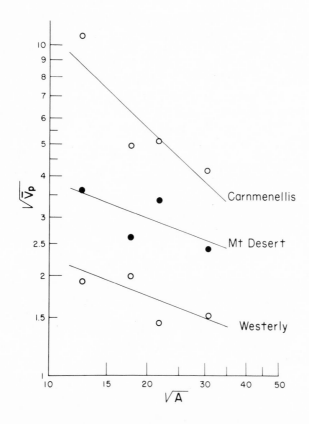

Fig. 9. Variation of log of average analytical error for major constituents ($\sqrt{\bar{V}_p}$) as a function of log of square root of measurement area ($\sqrt{A}$) for specimens of fine (Westerly), medium (Mt. Desert), and coarse (Carnmenellis) granite.

In addition to suggesting that the raw values ought to be transformed to logs before any further calculations, eqs. (8.1–8.3) indicate that we ought to compare $\bar{V}_p$ with A or $\sqrt{\bar{V}_p}$ with $\sqrt{A}$. As most readers will probably prefer to think of an error stated in the units of measurement, Fig. 9 shows the $\sqrt{\bar{V}_p}$ values for each specimen plotted against the appropriate values of $\sqrt{A}$.   Equations of the lines are

(Westerly) $\log \sqrt{\bar{V}_p} = 0.66528 - 0.16822 \log A$ (8.4)

(Mt. Desert) $\log \sqrt{\bar{V}_p} = 0.96844 - 0.18908 \log A$ (8.5)

(Carnmenellis) $\log \sqrt{\bar{V}_p} = 1.96424 - 0.46569 \log A$ (8.6)

The fit of the points in Fig. 9 is quite obviously far from perfect. Though sometimes large in an absolute sense, the deviations are quite reasonable in terms of the error expected in estimates of standard deviations based on small samples.   Most important, they do not appear to suggest systematic departure from linearity in the relation between $\log \bar{V}_p$ and $\log A$. (The interested reader may wish to convince himself that this cannot be said for the untransformed values shown in Table 8.1.)   We are thus finally in a position to estimate the effect of measurement area on analytical error in each of the three specimens.

9

A measure of coarseness
in the granitic fabric

1. THE DESIRABILITY OF A MEASURE OF COARSENESS

As a result of the work described in chapter 8 we are now in possession of empirical equations showing analytical error as a function of measurement area in each of three hand specimens. Granting that coarseness, however defined, is the same throughout each specimen, we have managed to characterize the effect of grain frequency on analytical error in each specimen, for it is clear that the number of grain sections will generally be proportional to the area of measurement. Now the specimens differ so widely in coarseness that they have been easily and successfully (or, at any rate, consistently) ranked by hand-specimen inspection; to date 34 out of 36 observers have ranked them identically.

We are thus in a position to make rather crude qualitative comparisons; for any particular measurement area, the analytical error of a thin-section analysis of a specimen intermediate in coarseness between any two of the test specimens may also be expected to be intermediate in size. Comparisons of this kind might be quite helpful to petrographers who happen to have specimens of the test rocks for comparison, but only such petrographers will be in a position to make and use them, and their number will be very small. The procedure, furthermore, is subject to very serious limitations stemming from the fact that, although inspection may lead to consistent ordering of unknown specimens in relation to the test specimens, it tells us nothing about the "distance" between any two specimens, known or unknown. We can guess about the order of an error for an unknown in relation to any standard; what we really need, however, is an estimate of the size of the error.

To obtain such an estimate we must either repeat on each unknown the procedure followed with the standards, or find some measure of coarseness which will not only tell us that an unknown lies some place between two of the standards but will permit us to guess *where* in this interval it lies.

The difficulties encountered in direct measurement of the fundamental variables—grain size or grain number—have already been described in considerable detail, and an account of the numerous unsuccessful attempts to make such measurements would serve no particular purpose. Instead, we shall present an account of the first successful detour of these obstacles. The measure of coarseness introduced here is certainly not the only possible one, and quite probably not the best one. At present, however, it is alone in its field and has the additional virtue of being simple to make and easy to use.

2. IC NUMBERS

The measure is simply the number of major mineral identity changes along a unit length of line. The changes are easily and quickly tabulated on the tape of a 10-key adding machine, a different number being assigned to each mineral species and printed out each time the mineral to which it is assigned passes under the cross-hair intersection in the course of the traverse. High magnification, as might be expected, adds slightly to the number of observed identity changes and enormously increases the nervous tension and fatigue. After a little practice—devoted chiefly to learning the keyboard of the adding machine—two and a half minutes suffice for the traverse of 40 mm. of a coarse rock, and five are more than enough for a traverse of similar length on the finest rock one is likely to attempt at medium magnification.

The full tally is, in effect, the number of changes of key an operator would make in carefully traversing the line with any one of the continuous line integrators described in chapter 3. It is of course greatly inflated by minor and accessory minerals. These are frequently fully or partially enclosed in the majors, so that a change is scored not only on passing from major to minor or accessory but also on re-entering the major.

Spurious tallies of this sort may account for 20 per cent of the total even in rocks of very low color index, and for more than a third of the total where the color index exceeds 10. The term "spurious" is used advisedly; grains of minor and accessory minerals are usually small in relation to single grains or continuous patches of the majors, and their habit is often such that their presence or absence can have little influence on the sampling variance of a major constituent. A plagioclase crystal which contains two flecks of sericite along the line of traverse, for instance, does not thereby become the sampling equivalent of three plagioclase grains. Yet it contributes three to the major mineral tally and five to the full total. Finally, the minor and accessory minerals are sometimes clustered, so that their contribution to the total tally may be highly erratic even over so small an area as a single thin section. For all these reasons it seems wise to delete not only minor and accessory mineral tallies but also the major mineral "returns" or "re-entries" occasioned by them. It is possible, of course, to refrain from recording both types in the first place. It is quicker to record them on the tape and eliminate them from the final tally, however, particularly if blank spaces have been distributed evenly through the tape to facilitate counting.

A rather careful test indicates that except possibly in very fine granites the identity change or "IC" numbers are sufficiently stable and reproducible for practical purposes. In the first stage of the test, forty thin sections, five from each of eight granites, were used. Each thin section was cut from a different hand specimen. The slides were randomly distributed among five blocks, each block containing one slide from each granite. As a precaution, all slides of four of the granites, also randomly selected, were done in duplicate. The analyses were thus broken into five groups of 12 each (4 single and 4 in duplicate). The order in which analyses were to be run within blocks was next randomized, and each block was then run separately, three on different days and two in the morning and after-noon of the same day, the actual microscope time per block amounting to about an hour and a half and the entire test extending over a period of eight days. The "main-" or "block-effect," which would reflect instability in the tabulation and identification conventions, proved negligible. Differences between granites were easily significant in relation to the variation of thin sections cut from the same granite. The "within-granite" variation was also much larger than the error of duplicates, so that the partial duplication actually contributed very little to the test.

Seven weeks later a new set of random blocks was set up with the same forty slides; the partial duplication of the first stage was abandoned, and to each of the blocks a thin section from each of three new granites was added. The order of measurement was then randomized within blocks, and the blocks were run, one or two a day, over a period of six days. The block effect was again negligible. Evidently the identification and tabulation conventions are suitably stable over a continuous working period of a week or so.

That this may not necessarily be so if the work is done sporadically over a considerably longer period of time is suggested by the Westerly and Pownal entries in Table 9.1, in which the full data are recorded. For Westerly, each September entry is smaller than the July value for the same slide, the average decrease being 11.6. In Pownal, on the other hand, each September entry is *higher* than the July value, the average increase being 8.6. In the other six granites included in both stages of the test the signs of the individual differences vary, and the average difference, whatever its sign, never exceeds 4.6. To date there is no satisfactory explanation of the Pownal and Westerly results. These two granites are by far the finest in the sample, so that a longer count is tallied in individual measurements made on them. Perhaps similar differences exist in the others but do not emerge simply because the individual counts are shorter. It is even remotely possible, though not likely, that the effect is purely random and requires no explanation. Time effects of this sort, frequently unexplained, are commonplace in other disciplines, and a paper by Griffiths and Rosenfeld (1954) suggests that they are not at all rare in geological work.

TABLE 9.1.   IC MEASUREMENTS ON SOME
TWO-FELDSPAR GRANITES

Granite	Individual Thin Sections					Average
Westerly, R. I.						
July	103	95	95	93	93	90.0
September	93	83	87	77	81	
Pownal, Me.						
July	68	60	48	77	57	66.3
September	80	62	55	81	75	
Elberton, Ga.						
July	49	56	62	62	49	55.1
September	58	52	64	47	52	
Fitzwilliam, N. H.						
July	52	56	54	44	55	51.7
September	51	46	48	48	63	
Milford, N. H.						
July	55	44	37	30	61	46.3
September	56	59	32	30	59	
Salisbury, N. C.						
July	30	35	41	51	30	35.1
September	25	29	37	38	35	
Woodbury, N. H.						
July	23	28	35	57	29	34.0
September	22	15	55	53	23	
Barre, Vt.						
July	40	26	31	35	26	33.6
September	32	40	27	35	44	
Bradford, R. I.						
September	53	41	62	58	56	54.0
Mt. Desert, Me.						
September	58	31	23	42	50	40.8
St. Pierre, Ile et Vilaine						
September	20	26	17	22	24	21.8

In any event, the difficulty is evidently restricted to rocks so fine that—as we shall shortly see—a precise estimate of IC will rarely be necessary. In the region in which good IC determinations are required there is no firm evidence of anything but random variation which can be controlled and reduced by replication; in this region the identification and tabulation conventions appear to be sufficiently stable over periods of the order of several weeks.

Several of the rocks listed in Table 9.1 are rather well known, and the assemblage of mean values should give the experienced petrographer a fair idea of how the IC numbers compare with his own grain-size designations.

For the three specimens used as standards in the area-variance study described in chapter 8, the IC numbers are

Westerly	87.8
Mt. Desert	46.0
Carnmenellis	20.8

These values are averages based on two traverses through each of 13 thin sections of each specimen, the traverses having been run separately at various times shortly before, during, or immediately after the work leading to the July results shown in Table 9.1.

3. THE RELATION BETWEEN IC NUMBERS AND ANALYTICAL ERROR

The work described in the previous section permits us to replace the qualitative grading of the coarseness of the three standard specimens with the observed IC numbers. In theory the IC scale extends from 1 to ∞, and Table 9.1 indicates that in practice it extends at least from 17 to 103. We cannot be sure, of course, that the intervals are equal along the scale, that a rock of IC 17, for instance, is "half" as fine as one of IC 34 in exactly the sense that one of IC 50 is "half" as fine as one of IC 100. The greater the number of grades, however, the less serious will be the trouble arising on this score. A scale extending in theory over an infinity of grades and in practice over more than 80 is surely preferable to one which contains only as many grades as there are items to be graded.

Assuming that departures from linearity in the scale are not serious, we must next inquire what relationship ought to pertain between IC number and analytical error. The IC tally is a linear frequency, and if an areal estimate were required the first thing to try would be $(IC)^2$. This is what we would do if we were given the linear frequency of a number of grains and asked to calculate the areal frequency. Now it is the *areal* frequency which is involved in eqs. (8.4–8.6), and if IC were to fulfill our fondest hopes it would be related to $\sqrt{\bar{V}_p}$ as $\sqrt{A}$ is. Thus we should expect an inverse linear variation between the logs of the IC values and the logs of the analytical errors for the three standards at any particular area of measurement. The latter are readily obtained by solving eqs. (8.4–8.6) for the desired area of measurement, and the IC values are listed at the close of the succeeding section. Table 9.2 shows the logs of the analytical errors for a number of areas for each of the three standards. From the measurements and estimates shown in the table we can now calculate new equations showing the regression of $\log \sqrt{\overline{V}_p}$ on $\log$ IC for each of the measurement areas. These equations are

$$\log \sqrt{\overline{V}} = 1.45131 - 0.65195 \log \text{IC, for } A = 960 \text{ mm.}^2 \quad (9.1)$$

$$\log \sqrt{\overline{V}} = 1.65168 - 0.74286 \log \text{IC, for } A = 625 \text{ mm.}^2 \quad (9.2)$$

$$\log \sqrt{\overline{V}} = 1.79468 - 0.80774 \log \text{IC, for } A = 480 \text{ mm.}^2 \quad (9.3)$$

$$\log \sqrt{\overline{V}} = 1.96406 - 0.88459 \log \text{IC, for } A = 320 \text{ mm.}^2 \quad (9.4)$$

$$\log \sqrt{\overline{V}} = 2.28765 - 1.03142 \log \text{IC, for } A = 160 \text{ mm.}^2 \quad (9.5)$$

TABLE 9.2.   LOG $\sqrt{\overline{V}_p}$ FOR DIFFERENT MEASUREMENT AREAS
IN THE THREE STANDARD SPECIMENS

Specimen	IC	log IC	$\log \sqrt{\overline{V}_p}$ for Indicated Measurement Areas, mm.²				
			160	320	480	625	960
Westerly	87.8	1.94349	0.29450	0.24386	0.21424	0.19495	0.16360
Mt. Desert	46.0	1.66276	0.55168	0.49477	0.46147	0.43980	0.40455
Carnmenellis	20.8	1.31806	0.93780	0.79762	0.71562	0.66223	0.57543

The graphs of these lines and the points from which they were calculated (data of Table 9.2) are shown in Fig. 10. It is evident that the points do not lie exactly along straight lines, but the departure from linearity, which is quite possibly systematic, is very small.

A considerable body of supporting evidence, most of it dating from long before this study was begun, suggests that the precision errors yielded by eqs. (9.1–9.5) are quite realistic. In rather large suites of specimens from Westerly, R. I., Mt. Desert, Me., Salisbury, N, C., and St. Pierre, Ile et Vilaine (France), and also in a small group from Bradford, R. I., two or three thin sections per specimen had been cut and analysed in the course of other work. The square root of the mean square for error (or discrepancy) in the variance analysis of each of these suites is an estimate of the same parameter here estimated by calculation of $\sqrt{\overline{V}_p}$ for a large number of sections, all cut from the same specimen. Measurement of IC and calculation of $\sqrt{\bar{V}_a}$ in each suite thus yield five independent determinations which may serve as a check on eqs. (9.1–9.5).

The comparison is made in Table 9.3. In evaluating the table it will be well to bear in mind that the error attaching to *all* the entries, both observed and predicted, is very large. Indeed, it is rather surprising that the sequence of observed values is so similar to that of the predicted ones. It may nevertheless be noted that in four of the five comparisons the observed value is appreciably smaller than the predicted and in the fifth

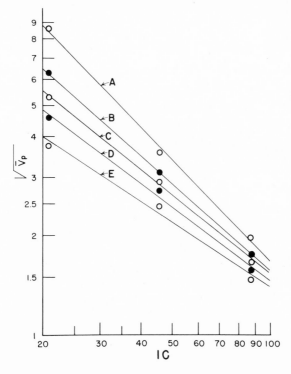

Fig. 10. log of estimated average major mineral analytical error ($\sqrt{\bar{V}_p}$) as a function of log of coarseness (IC) for different measurement areas: *A*, 160 mm²; *B*, 320 mm²; *C*, 480 mm²; *D*, 625 mm²; *E*, 960 mm².

the excess of observed over predicted is slight. Although the number of comparisons is too small to permit an accurate test, this is surely a strong hint that any bias in the equations is toward an overestimate of precision error. It would of course be preferable to have no bias at all, but in the present status of modal analysis a bias leading to a little more work and a little more caution in attributing significance to small differences will do no great harm.

TABLE 9.3.   COARSENESS (IC), PREDICTED $[E(\sqrt{\overline{V}_p})]$ AND OBSERVED $(\sqrt{\overline{V}_d})$ HAND-SPECIMEN PRECISION IN SOME TWO-FELDSPAR GRANITES

Granite	Number of Specimens	IC	$E(\sqrt{\overline{V}_p})$	$\sqrt{\overline{V}_d}$
Westerly, R. I.	11	90	1.6	1.3
Bradford, R. I.	5	54	2.4	1.3
Mt. Desert, Me.	18	41	2.5	2.7
Salisbury, N. C.	21	35	3.6	2.4
St. Pierre, Ile et Vilaine	12	22	3.8	2.9

It should be remembered, too, that the predicted value is an *average* error. In the data from which Table 9.3 was obtained, what is designed as an estimate of average error actually agrees better with the *largest* major constituent error for each of the suites concerned.   Specifically:

Granite	Largest Major Constituent Error	$E(\sqrt{\overline{V}_p})$
Westerly	1.5	1.6
Bradford	1.4	2.4
Mt. Desert	3.2	2.5
Salisbury	2.9	3.6
St. Pierre	3.0	3.8

We may conclude that eqs. (9.1–9.5) provide a usable, if rather conservative, approximation of the relation between IC numbers and $\sqrt{\overline{V}_p}$ for different measurement areas.   With this information it is a relatively simple matter to maintain the analytical error of hand-specimen means at or below some fixed value by varying the number of thin sections cut from each in accord with its IC number.   The procedure by which the amount of replication necessary for control of analytical error may be determined is described in the next chapter.

10

The control
of analytical error
by replication

1. Maintaining Analytical Error of Hand-Specimen Averages at or below a Fixed Level

Whenever interest attaches to some measurable property of individual items in a sample it is advantageous if the precision of the estimate of this property is comparable in all items. In many petrographic problems the hand specimen is the individual item, and the more important the problem the more likely are we to examine the individual results rather closely; examples include studies of variation of composition with distance from base line or plane, such as a contact, the plotting of results in ternary or other variation diagrams, and the occasional attempts to construct composition contours on a geographic base. It is true that we still rarely make the type of statistical calculation which presupposes uniformity of subgroup variance, and usually do not even plan our observations so that this form of calculation is a meaningful activity. This, however, does not in any way guard us against mistakes and faulty interpretations arising from inhomogeneous subgroup variance, for we are usually obliged to attribute equal weight to the individual observations wherever more than a few of them are to be compared without benefit of calculation.

It would be an exceedingly tedious matter to adjust the area of measurement and the number of thin sections per specimen so that means of hand specimens of differing coarseness could be presumed to be of *equal* precision, but from the work of the preceding section a schedule of replication can be developed which will maintain the precision error of the hand-specimen means *at or below* some fixed level. Solving eq. (9.1) for even integral values of $\bar{V}$ in the range $2 \leqslant \bar{V} \leqslant 18$ gives the IC values shown in the third column of Table 10.1 Thus the precision error of a

79

thin section cut from a rock of IC 93 is 2.0 as a variance or 1.41 as a standard deviation. For a rock of IC 59, the appropriate variance is 4.0 and the standard deviation 2.00. (For intermediate values of IC the sampling error will also have some intermediate value.)

TABLE 10.1. IC FOR EVEN INTEGRAL VALUES OF $\bar{V}$ IN EQ. $(9.1)^a$

$\bar{V}_p$	$\sqrt{\bar{V}_p}$	IC	$l_{\bar{V}=2}$	$l_{\bar{V}=4}$	$l_{\bar{V}=6}$
2	1.41	93	1		
4	2.00	59	2	1	
6	2.45	44	3		1
8	2.83	36	4	2	
10	3.16	31	5		
12	3.46	27	6	3	2
14	3.74	24	7		
16	4.00	22	8	4	
18	4.24	20	9		3

^{a} $A = 960$ mm.^{2}; for explanation of l, see text below.

Since the variance of a mean varies inversely with the number of items on which it is based, if we wanted means of equal precision for a pair of specimens having these IC numbers, we would use twice as many thin sections for the one with IC 59 as we used for the one with IC 93. Generalizing this procedure, to find the number of thin sections per specimen required to reduce the sampling variance of hand-specimen means of coarser rocks to the level reached with a single thin section at IC 93, we simply divide each of the succeeding variances in the table by the first. The results of this division are shown in the column headed $l_{\bar{V}=2}$; if we wanted optimum[1] precision estimates of two specimens, one with IC 36 and the other with IC 27, for instance, we would analyze four thin sections of the first and six of the second.

If a precision variance of 4 (standard deviation of 2 per cent) in the specimen mean is tolerable, the column headed $l_{\bar{V}=4}$ in the table shows that one thin section per specimen will be adequate for IC 59, two for $60 > $ IC $\geqslant 35$, and so forth. If a precision variance of 6 (standard deviation of 2.45) is sufficient, the column headed $l_{\bar{V}=6}$ gives the replication schedule.

Following the same procedure with eqs. (9.2–9.5), we find the amount of replication required to maintain the specimen precision error at or below 1.4, 2.0, and 2.5 per cent for the measurement area listed to the right of

[1] The term "optimum" is here used as an abbreviation for "precision obtainable with a single thin section of large area cut from a very fine rock."

each equation. The most convenient way to summarize these results is by charts such as Figs. 11–13. Those who customarily work at a particular measurement area may prefer some simplification of this scheme. Tables showing the range of IC values for different values of l and $\sqrt{\bar{V}}$ are easily prepared. Those who prefer graphs to charts or tables may like to know

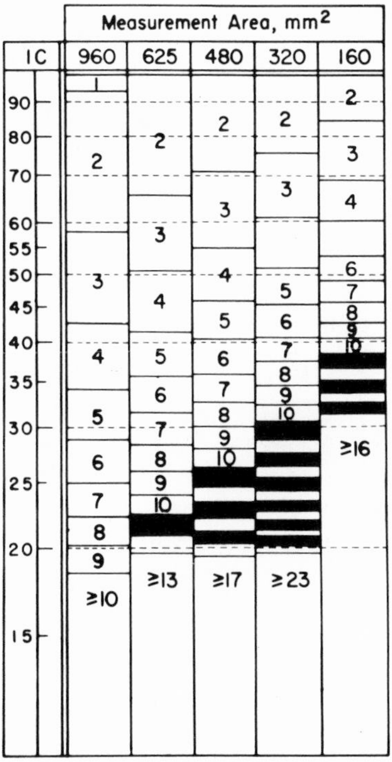

	Measurement Area, mm²				
IC	960	625	480	320	160
90	1				2
80		2	2	2	
70	2				3
60		3	3	3	4
55					
50	3	4	4		6
45		4		5	7
40	4	5	5	6	8 9 10
35		5 6	6	7 8	
30	5	7	8	9 10	
25	6 7 8	8 9 10	9 10		≥16
20	9				
	≥10	≥13	≥17	≥23	
15					

Fig. 11.

Replication schedule for maintaining analytical error ≤1.41. The coarseness scale (IC) is shown at the left. Subsequent columns indicate the number of thin sections (of size shown by column headings) per hand specimen required to maintain average major mineral analytical error ≤1.41. For a specimen having IC 45, for instance, three 960-mm² measurement areas are required. If the measurement area is 480 mm² per slide, five slides will be required, and so forth.

that a plot of the l values in any column of Table 10.1 against the appropriate $\sqrt{\bar{V}}$ entries is very nearly linear on log-log paper, and this holds also for similar calculations with eqs. (9.2–9.5).

It is to be remembered that by operating according to Figs. 11–13 we do not equalize the precision error but merely maintain it *at or below* some fixed maximum. In evaluating data obtained in this fashion, those who rely on inspection need only substitute for the usual tacit assumption of uniform error (equal weight) the notion that the error attached to each result is *equal to or less than* some fixed amount.

The specimen variances are still, strictly speaking, inhomogeneous, but their inhomogeneity is not enough to upset interpretations of significance tests based on variance analysis unless very large samples are used or exact probabilities are indispensable. Commonly, neither of these conditions holds.

This is a good place to indulge in a little clarification of terminology. When we "maintain precision," even at an exact value, by replication, the precision error we have reference to is that which characterizes the

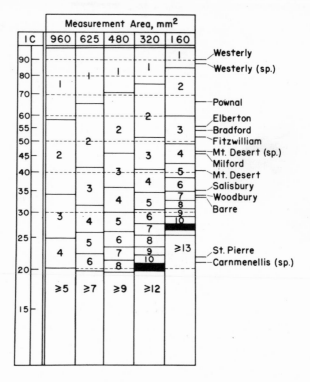

Fig. 12. Replication schedule for maintaining average major mineral analytical error ≤2.0. Along the right margin measured IC values are indicated for a number of well-known granites.

parent, not that actually found in any particular sample. Observed specimen precision variances ought to be compatible with the value indicated by the IC number and the amount of replication used, in the sense that they might have been drawn from a parent characterized by this value; except in rare and fortuitous instances agreement will not be exact. There is, of course, no need for exact agreement; the homogeneity of subgroup variances presupposed in analyses of variance concerns the parent, not the sample.

2. Choosing a Precision Standard

The precision standards set up in Figs. 11–13, though perhaps not greatly different in an absolute sense, make very different demands on the analyst. A petrographer planning to use any one of them will find the work either prohibitive or, to say the least, discouraging, unless the minimum

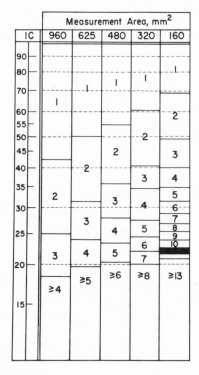

Fig. 13.

Replication schedule for maintaining average major mineral analytical error $\leqslant 2.45$.

measurement area on his thin sections is of the order of $\frac{3}{4}$ in.^{2}. Numerical comparisons used in this section are based exclusively on measurement areas of 1 and $1\frac{1}{2}$ in.^{2}; those who may be obliged to use smaller measurement areas can make similar comparisons from the charts.

A. Modal analyses of chemically analyzed specimens. Here it seems reasonable to suggest that the petrographic work should be of the highest grade, particularly if the chemical analysis is of interest primarily as an index of modal composition. Unless the rock is so coarse that microscopic analysis is out of the question, a specimen mode of parent error $\sqrt{\overline{V}_p} = 1.41$ can hardly compare in cost with a first-grade chemical analysis. Figure 11 shows that, even for IC 20, only 9 thin sections of $1\frac{1}{2}$ in.^{2} area or 12 of 1 in.^{2} will be required. For the vast majority of medium-grained plutonic rocks, no more than 4 or 5 of the former and 6 or 7 of the latter will be needed.   However much the petrographer pays for his sections and however highly he values his time, the cost of a mode which meets the standards of Fig. 11 will usually be very much less than the cost of a norm of the same specimen.

It may be argued that such concentration of effort on a single specimen is wasteful, no matter how inexpensive in an absolute sense.   It is important to realize, however, that there is little basis for a direct comparison of mode and norm unless both describe the same sample.   If the mode is an average based on slides cut from a number of specimens, as is perhaps most commonly the case, this is not true except on the assumption that the specimens are identical.   Now this is a most unlikely hypothesis, one which most petrographers would strongly reject in any other situation.   Why is it so often considered appropriate in this one?

B. Detailed petrographic research.   Comparison of Figs. 11 and 12 shows that it is much easier to maintain $\sqrt{\overline{V}_p} \leqslant 2.0$ than $\leqslant 1.4$.   For $1\frac{1}{2}$ in.^{2} measurement areas, one thin section per specimen will maintain $\sqrt{\overline{V}_p} \leqslant 2.0$ over most of the range in which two are necessary to hold it to $\leqslant 1.4$; similarly, two sections per specimen will usually replace three or four indicated by Fig. 11, and so forth.   Even for large thin sections, the amount of replication indicated by Fig. 11 is enough to discourage or seriously limit work on medium and coarse rocks.   The situation is far worse if it is necessary to use measurement areas of only 1 in.^{2}.   The schedule set up in Fig. 12 seems much more reasonable.   For measurement areas of 1 in.^{2} this schedule is only slightly more demanding in the intermediate IC range, but 5 or 6 sections per specimen may be needed in coarser rocks, and this is probably asking too much.   If large thin sections are available—and there is no good reason why they should not be—maintaining $\sqrt{\overline{V}_p} \leqslant 2.0$ seems perfectly feasible.

C. Reconnaissance work.   Figure 13 may be used when detailed comparisons are not contemplated or when differences between specimens are known to be very large.   For $1\frac{1}{2}$-in.^{2} measurement areas, however, substitution of Fig. 13 for Fig. 12 will never reduce the number of slides per specimen by more than 1, and often it will not even do this.   The same holds for 1-in.^{2} areas except at the very bottom of the observed IC range. As we have seen, reducing $\sqrt{\overline{V}_p}$ from 2.0 to 1.4 entails a considerable and very often impractical amount of work.   Reducing $\sqrt{\overline{V}_p}$ from 2.5 to 2.0, on the other hand, will never require much additional work, and over large (discontinuous) parts of the range it will require none.   Given thin sections of suitable area, it is difficult to imagine a petrographer willing to maintain $\sqrt{\overline{V}_p} \leqslant 2.5$, but unwilling to maintain it $\leqslant 2.0$. A hypo-thetical situation can be constructed, in which such behavior would be perfectly proper, particularly if it is necessary to use small sections. It might then be even more proper to set about getting good thin sections.

3. MAINTAINING MAXIMUM PRECISION OF THE MEAN OF A GROUP OF SPECIMENS AND FIXED PRECISION OF THE INDIVIDUAL RESULTS

If all the hand specimens are essential to a study and it is necessary to maintain the precision of the hand-specimen values, then of course the laboratory cost[2] varies exactly as the number of thin sections required per specimen. Such a situation may arise, for instance, where only a few specimens have been collected from a large mass, or where a great many have been taken with a view to preparing a detailed composition contour map. In the first case the additional laboratory cost will rarely be excessive. In the second it may easily be prohibitive; field work of this sort undertaken without enough advance information to give at least a good approximation of laboratory cost is very likely to be wasted.

If the primary objective is simply a well-established mean value for the rock, based on hand-specimen values whose precision has been maintained at a reasonable level by the use of replicate sections per specimen, much of the cost of the replication can be balanced by appropriate reduction of the number of specimens. Most attempts to characterize the composition and variability of reasonably homogeneous rocks are of this type. Interest centers both in the mean for the rock and in the size and nature of point-to-point variation within the mass. In the latter connection it is far better to work with small or moderate numbers of specimen averages of small precision error than to rely on great numbers of specimen estimates, each subject to large precision error. If this can be accomplished without enlarging the error of the group mean, little will be lost and much may be gained by reduction in the number of specimens examined. Now the reduction in sample size and increase in replication per specimen can in fact be balanced so that the precision of the sample mean is maintained. The procedure always increases the total number of analyses required unless there is no point-to-point variation whatever in the rock. But unless this type of variation is rather large the increase in number of analyses, and hence in laboratory cost, is often modest.

The variance of a mean based on k thin sections of each of n hand specimens is

$$\sigma_1{}^2 = \frac{\sigma_b{}^2}{n} + \frac{\sigma_a{}^2}{nk} \tag{10.1}$$

[2] "Cost" here signifies both financial expense and labor time.

where $\sigma_b{}^2$ is the variance of the specimens (the *between-specimen* variance) and $\sigma_a{}^2$ is the variance of thin sections cut from the same specimen (the *within-specimen* variance).   The preceding sections of this chapter are concerned with the effect of coarseness, as characterized by IC number, on $\sigma_a{}^2$, which we have elsewhere defined as the *analytical error* of modal analysis.

From a different number of specimens (m) and thin sections per specimen (l) of the same rock, we would obtain a mean with error $\sigma_2{}^2$, where

$$\sigma_2{}^2 = \frac{\sigma_b{}^2}{m} + \frac{\sigma_a{}^2}{ml}$$

By substitution and rearrangement of terms, it may be shown (see Cameron, 1951, pp. 92–93) that, if $\sigma_1{}^2$ and $\sigma_2{}^2$ are to be identical, the condition

$$\frac{m}{n} = \frac{\Phi + \dfrac{1}{l}}{\Phi + \dfrac{1}{k}} \tag{10.2}$$

must be satisfied, where $\Phi = \sigma_b{}^2/\sigma_a{}^2$, the ratio of between- to within-specimen variance.   If this relation is satisfied, the parent precision of a mean based on k sections of each of n specimens will be the same as that of one based on l sections of each of m specimens.

Denoting by N the total number of analyses, we have that $nk = N$, and $(1/n) = (k/N)$.   Accordingly, we may rewrite eq. (10.1) as

$$\sigma_1{}^2 = \frac{1}{N} (k\sigma_b{}^2 + \sigma_a{}^2)$$

and since $k \geqslant 1$ it is evident from inspection that $\sigma_1{}^2$ is least when $k = 1$.[3] For any particular value of N, therefore, the best estimate of a group mean will be obtained when $k = 1$, $n = N$, so that a single thin section is cut from each hand specimen.   If, in eq. (10.2), $k = 1$ and $l \geqslant 2$ the fraction m/n indicates the proportion of the original sample from each of which l sections must be cut, if the parent error of the sample mean is to be held to its minimum value at the same time that the analytical error of the specimen means is to be maintained at or below some particular level by replication.   If a number of specimens intermediate between m and n is used, the error of the sample mean will be less than for single sectioning of n specimens.

This relation may be tabled in a variety of ways, and the procedure used here is based on the present state of knowledge in the field.   From the

---

[3] Unless, of course, $\sigma_b{}^2 = 0$, so that the partition of analyses within and among specimens is of no consequence.

work described in earlier sections of this chapter we are in possession of fairly good estimates of σ_a, the analytical error, as a function of an easily measured statistic (IC) closely related to coarseness. By means of Figs. 11–13 and a determination of the IC number we may find an l which will maintain the precision error of specimen estimates at or below any of three values.

On the other hand, present knowledge of σ_b, the variation between hand specimens of the same rock, is hopelessly inadequate. It seems most useful, therefore, to display the relations between m/n and l for the three levels of analytical error already used in Figs. 11–13 and a wide range of σ_b, and this is what has been done in Tables 10.2–10.4. Each of these tables covers one of the analytical-error levels (σ_a), and in each $0.5 \leqslant \sigma_b \leqslant 5.0$. Point-to-point variations characterized by $\sigma_b < 0.5$ would be negligible in almost any practical problem, whereas σ_b much in excess of 5.0 should certainly be infrequent in well-defined rock types. Where it is so large, differences between specimens will almost certainly be apparent before microscopic examination. Whatever the final geological or petrological interpretation of these differences, it may be useful for analytical purposes to subdivide the sample. A glance at Tables 10.2–10.4 shows at once that m/n increases rapidly with increase in σ_b.

The remarks on terminology at the conclusion of the first section of this chapter apply also, though in somewhat more complicated fashion, to the argument of this one. Tables 10.2–10.4 are simply algebraic consequences of the definition of $\sigma_{\bar{x}}$, the error of the mean; the use of parameter symbols for the within- and between-specimen standard deviations in these tables is thus quite legitimate. In any practical situation, however, we can only decide which line of which table is to be used by means of a

TABLE 10.2.   PERCENTAGE OF SPECIMENS TO BE RETAINED FOR OPTIMUM PRECISION OF THE SAMPLE MEAN WHEN l THIN SECTIONS ARE REQUIRED TO INSURE $\sigma_a \leqslant 1.41$, FOR $0.5 \leqslant \sigma_b \leqslant 5.0$

σ_b	l for $\sigma_a \leqslant 1.41$							
	2	3	4	5	6	7	8	9
0.50	0.56	0.41	0.33	0.29	0.26	0.24	0.22	0.21
1.00	0.66	0.56	0.50	0.47	0.44	0.43	0.42	0.41
1.41	0.75	0.66	0.62	0.60	0.58	0.57	0.56	0.56
2.00	0.83	0.78	0.75	0.73	0.72	0.71	0.71	0.70
2.45	0.88	0.83	0.81	0.80	0.79	0.79	0.78	0.78
3.00	0.91	0.89	0.86	0.85	0.85	0.84	0.84	0.84
4.00	0.94	0.93	0.92	0.91	0.91	0.90	0.90	0.90
5.00	0.96	0.95	0.94	0.94	0.94	0.94	0.94	0.93

series of guesses or experimental determinations.   This is very often true in other fields of inquiry, and the matter has now been aired so fully that it can hardly cause much confusion.

TABLE 10.3.   PERCENTAGE OF SPECIMENS TO BE RETAINED
FOR OPTIMUM PRECISION OF THE SAMPLE MEAN
WHEN l THIN SECTIONS ARE REQUIRED TO INSURE
$\sigma_a \leqslant 2.00$, FOR $0.5 \leqslant \sigma_b \leqslant 5.0$

σ_b	l for $\sigma_a \leqslant 2.0$			
	2	3	4	5
0.50	0.53	0.37	0.29	0.25
1.00	0.60	0.47	0.40	0.36
1.41	0.67	0.56	0.50	0.47
2.00	0.75	0.67	0.62	0.60
2.45	0.80	0.73	0.70	0.68
3.00	0.85	0.79	0.77	0.75
4.00	0.90	0.87	0.85	0.84
5.00	0.93	0.91	0.90	0.89

TABLE 10.4.   PERCENTAGE OF SPECIMENS TO BE RETAINED
FOR OPTIMUM PRECISION OF THE SAMPLE MEAN
WHEN l THIN SECTIONS ARE REQUIRED TO INSURE
$\sigma_a \leqslant 2.45$, FOR $0.5 \leqslant \sigma_b \leqslant 5.0$

σ_b	l for $\sigma_a \leqslant 2.45$		
	2	3	4
0.50	0.52	0.36	0.28
1.00	0.57	0.43	0.36
1.41	0.62	0.50	0.44
2.00	0.70	0.60	0.55
2.45	0.75	0.67	0.62
3.00	0.79	0.71	0.68
4.00	0.86	0.82	0.80
5.00	0.90	0.87	0.85

4. LIMITATIONS OF THE METHOD

The standards of precision established by the charts and tables presented in the preceding sections range from a level beyond that required by most petrographic research to one which should be regarded as a minimum in work purporting to be "quantitative."   As they have not yet been applied practically, we shall have to rest content with some guessing about how they might be used in specific situations. Before beginning this, however, it may be helpful to state explicitly some of the limitations of the technique.

The principal limitation is that the IC number as defined here applies only to three major constituents present in roughly equivalent amounts in the granitic fabric; further, it applies to no one of the major constituents but is rather a measure of their average frequency and an index of their *average* variability.[4]

It is obvious that the product of a measuring technique defined without reference to orientation can have meaning only where orientation is weak or lacking. In a banded or foliated rock, or even in one with powerful lineation of a major constituent, the IC number will almost certainly vary widely depending on the direction of the line along which it is measured. It is quite possible that the method could be modified to accommodate certain types of orientation, but modification, and probably rather extensive modification, will be necessary.

In eucrystalline rocks markedly porphyritic texture might cause trouble even if the phenocrysts were not oriented, but the trouble may not be as severe as might be expected. Occasional large crystals will of course reduce the observed IC number and thus indicate the need for replication; the effect is in the right direction, but whether it is usually sufficient, excessive or inadequate remains to be determined.

The justification for adopting the IC number as a measure of coarseness is simply that usable specifications of the boundaries of single grains are not available. Where this difficulty does not exist—as in certain sediments or microporphyritic lavas and dikes—it should be possible to devise an index of coarseness which has a more immediate physical significance.

5. COUNT LENGTH

The work described in chapters 8–10 was designed in the hope that the counting error could be extracted, so that tables consisting exclusively of within-specimen sampling variance components could be prepared and these then combined with any chosen counting variance. This was finally abandoned for the reason that the *total* variance of results for the two larger measurement areas of Westerly was less than the expected counting variance. This could be a chance event, of course, but it is also possible, as was suggested at the close of chapter 5, that the true counting error is somewhat less than binomial; there was a weak indication of this

---

[4] At present it is not even known how well the technique will work in one-feldspar granites, for in these only one constituent, quartz, lies in the appropriate composition range, and the IC number will be much reduced because there are only two major constituents instead of three.

in the original test (Chayes, 1949, pp. 6–7), and the binomial error is calculated without reference to the fact that the points are symmetrically distributed over the face of the slide.

In any event, the counting variance could not be subtracted from two of the total variances and was finally allowed to stand in all of them; the argument has been developed with no attempt to separate sampling and counting components in σ_a, the analytical error. A further examination of σ_a may nevertheless be of interest to many readers. σ_a contains two identifiable components, one expressing the true variation among thin sections of the same specimen, the other representing the error of the count (or other procedure) by means of which the thin sections are analyzed. Symbolically, the error attaching to any single result is

$$\sigma_a = \sqrt{\sigma_\omega{}^2 + \sigma_c{}^2}$$

where c designates the counting and ω the true within-specimen variance. For the point counter, σ_c is very nearly $\{p(1-p)/n\}^{1/2}$ so that, to a good approximation

$$\sigma_a{}^2 = \frac{\sigma_\omega{}^2}{l} + \frac{p(1-p)}{ln}$$

where σ_a is the error of a specimen mean based on l thin sections each analyzed with a count of length n.

If σ_ω is very small, most of the observed variation is introduced by the count, but the influence of the count diminishes rapidly as σ_ω increases. For $n = 600$, $p = 0.3$, approximately the situation in most of the work reported here, if $\sigma_\omega = 0$, $\sigma_a = 1.87$, whereas for $\sigma_\omega = 3$, σ_a is only 3.54. The difference $\sigma_a - \sigma_\omega$ of course decreases with increase in n, but the decrease is not rapid, and by itself would not be a powerful argument for extending the count length. For $n = 1800$ instead of 600 in the example just given, for instance, if $\sigma_\omega = 0$, $\sigma_a = 1.08$, whereas for $\sigma_\omega = 3$, $\sigma_a = 3.27$.

As n increases, the sensitivity of σ_c and hence of σ_a to differences in p tends to decrease also, and this is in some respects more of an advantage than the slight increase in precision. For $\sigma_\omega = 3$, $n = 600$, $\sigma_a = 3.42$ at $p = 0.2$ and 3.60 at $p = 0.4$; if $n = 1800$, however, $\sigma_a = 3.14$ at $p = 0.2$ and 3.21 at $p = 0.4$. If there are real differences in p from specimen to specimen, as will be the case when $\sigma_b > 0$, it is useful to hold their effect on σ_a to a minimum, particularly when, as in most variance analysis, σ_a is estimated from a mean square which contains contributions from every specimen in the sample. The desirability of a result continuous in the tenths place is sufficient justification for a count length in excess of 1000. The decreased sensitivity of σ_a to differences in p is perhaps additional justification for making the excess as large as practical. Very little is gained by extending the count past 2000 unless interest centers on the accessory minerals.

As often happens in measurement problems, systematic sampling technique in point-counting is based primarily on practical considerations. A systematic sample of the measurement area is intuitively more appealing than a simple-random sample, but the controlling factor is the use of spring levers riding on notched wheels for locating the points. This arrangement automatically yields a two-dimensional systematic sample, and it is something of a nuisance to try to make it do anything else.

It happens, however, that the situation is one in which systematic sampling should be somewhat superior to simple random sampling. A single analysis may be regarded as a tally of n equally spaced points along each of k equidistant lines. Each line is thus itself an analysis of count length n. The variance along lines will be $N/n = k$ times as large as the variance of the full result. Similarly, along any line the variance within the interval between points (l) will be $nl/l = n$ times as large as the variance for the full line. In theory, systematic sampling is more precise than simple random sampling if the variance within the subsamples is larger than the population variance as a whole. It would thus seem that the counting error, instead of being strictly binomial, ought to be *no larger than binomial*. The advantage of systematic sampling will almost certainly vary with coarseness. For a fixed interval between points the efficiency of the systematic sampling presumably increases with decrease in IC. Even the full binomial counting error contributes little to the total variance where σ_ω is appreciable, however, so that precisely when the effect is strongest it would be most difficult to isolate. Except for the two larger measurement areas of Westerly, in which the total within-specimen variance is closer to the counting variance for 900 points than for the 660 actually used, none of the work reported here gives any indication of the gain in efficiency owing to systematic sampling, or of the variation in this gain with change in IC. In the face of all these complexities it is perhaps just as well that the plan to extract a binomial counting-error variance from each of the observed $\bar{V}_p$ values had to be abandoned.

6. THE SIZE AND COST OF THIN SECTIONS

From the charts, the tables, and the preceding discussion, it is evident that there is nearly always some advantage in using a large measurement area. Whether this advantage is sufficient to compensate for the additional cost of large slides will depend both on the coarseness of the rock involved and the type of information desired. If the problem is simply to obtain an estimate of some specific precision for a single specimen, the advantage of the larger measurement area is hardly material unless the specimen is exceedingly coarse. The petrographer accustomed to working on thin sections of $\frac{3}{4}$-in.^{2} area, for instance, will find that enlarging the measurement area to $1\frac{1}{2}$ in.^{2} will never more than halve the number of sections he must analyze, that such a reduction is quite unusual, and that quite often, particularly in finer-grained rocks, the number required will be the same.

If it is necessary to maintain precision in a large number of specimen averages, of course, even a small reduction in the number of thin sections (and analyses) per specimen may be of some importance. In a rock of IC 35, for instance, the choice would be between 4 large sections and 7 small ones to maintain $\sqrt{\overline{V}_p} \leqslant 1.4$, between 2 and 4 to maintain it $\leqslant 2.0$, and between 2 and 3 to maintain it $\leqslant 2.5$. Percentage-wise, these reductions are quite appreciable; a man called on for even a few dozen specimen values with $\sqrt{\overline{V}} \leqslant 2.0$, for instance, might feel that a reduction of 50 per cent in the number of slides was a worthwhile economy.

The real value of the larger areas, however, and one which will often far more than compensate for their increased cost, emerges from Tables 10.2–10.4 in which the analyses are allocated so as to maintain both fixed precision in the specimen values and maximum precision in the mean. If $\sigma_a \leqslant 2.0$, $\sigma_b = 0.5$, for instance, and the measurement areas and IC are again such that the small areas must be done in quadruplicate and the large ones in duplicate, Table 10.3 indicates that $\{(4)(0.29) - (2)(0.53)\}$ $/(4)(0.29)$, or only 8 per cent fewer large slides will be required, *but these may be distributed over* $(0.53 - 0.29)/0.29$, *or 82 per cent more specimens.* With increase of σ_b the increase in the number of specimens over which the work may be distributed drops off, but the saving in total number of slides and analyses improves. The full comparison is shown in Table 10.5. In round numbers, the extremes of the table indicate that the large slides

TABLE 10.5.   ADVANTAGE OF $1\frac{1}{2}$-in.^{2} MEASUREMENT AREA PER SLIDE OVER $\frac{3}{4}$ in.^{2} FOR IC 35.5, $\sigma_a = 2.0$ AND $0.5 \leqslant \sigma_b \leqslant 5.0$

σ_b	Per Cent Reduction in Total Number of Slides	Per Cent Increase in Number of Specimens Analyzed
0.50	8	83
1.00	25	50
1.41	33	34
2.00	40	21
2.45	43	14
3.00	45	10
4.00	47	6
5.00	48	3

may permit the examination of almost twice as many specimens if σ_b is small and may almost halve the total number of slides required if σ_b is large. For intermediate values of σ_b both reduction in the number of analyses and expansion in the number of specimens analyzed are appreciable.

Any large consumer or manufacturer of thin sections can provide figures which will show whether a particular reduction in the total number of slides will compensate for the increase in the cost of the larger slides. The money (or labor) cost of analyzing thin sections will vary greatly from analyst to analyst, and its importance will often depend on the personal situation of the analyst. Except in a highly specific context it is impossible to attach a money value to the increase in the number of specimens analyzed, but in a scientific sense this alone may be worth far more than the increased cost of the thin sections. Quite often it may represent the difference between success and failure, between results which are fairly conclusive and those which are merely provocative or perhaps even misleading.

7. Effect of Coarseness on the Scale of Petrographic Investigation

Analytical error increases much more rapidly with decrease in IC number than with decrease in measurement area, and Figs. 11–13 are primarily designed to provide guidance in connection with the planning of quantitative studies of coarser rocks. Here the importance of measurement area is so evident as to require no comment. The petrologist concerned with coarse-grained rocks will usually be well advised to insist on measurement areas as large as can be traversed in a single setting of his integrating stage or point counter. By the same token, if he is obliged to use an instrument which permits the traverse of only a small area per setting, he probably should refrain from analyzing coarse rocks.

Even if large thin sections are available, however, it is evident that much more replication will be required for coarse than for fine rocks. In the matter of obtaining modes for comparison with norms or other calculated parameters, for instance, Fig. 11 shows that it would be four times as expensive to work, say, on the Carnmenellis granite as on the Westerly. Considering the scarcity of chemical analyses this additional expense is certainly justifiable, and no sensible petrographer will begrudge a few additional hours at the microscope in such a worthy cause.

If our interest is the commoner one of establishing a good mean value from numerous individual results of known reliability, however, the fourfold increase in the number of analyses entails a much larger investment of time. Figure 12 shows that a single thin section per specimen will be sufficient for Westerly whereas four will be required for each specimen of Carnmenellis. Suppose, now, that we have collected 20 specimens of each.   We actually have no need for a Carnmenellis average based on 80 analyses when our Westerly average is based on only 20.   If we specify that the Carnmenellis average is to be as reliable as the Westerly, Table 10.3 shows that we should use $(0.29)(20) = 6$ specimens of Carnmenellis if σ_b in each mass is of the order of 0.5, 8 if σ_b is 1.0, 10 if it is 1.4, 14 if it is 2.45, etc.

Thus, if we suppose that there is very little variation within each mass —which seems to be substantially true in most of the smaller granite plutons—the additional cost of working on the Carnmenellis is very slight, and the marked reduction in the number of specimens examined is not likely to be of much consequence.   Note, however, that the expense increases very rapidly with increase in σ_b; for $\sigma_b = 2.0$ it is already necessary to retain 13 of the Carnmenellis specimens, so that the mean value for Carnmenellis is 52/20 or 2.6 times as costly as the Westerly mean, and we still have only 13/20 or 65 per cent as much information about the point-to-point variation.

This is an extreme example and purposely chosen as one.   In the present stage of development the real importance of Fig. 12 is as an indication that such contrasts in efficiency will *not* arise in the study of vast amounts of plutonic rock.   Maintenance of analytical error $\leqslant 2.0$ requires no more than three or less than two large thin sections per specimen in eight of the twelve rocks in which IC has so far been measured.   Difficulties of this sort will of course be encountered as the technique is extended to coarser rocks.   The areal geologist, who may not ignore a rock simply because it is coarse, must learn how to deal with the problem.

It is obvious that the same expenditure of money and effort nets larger returns in the finer-grained rocks, and that we shall find out as much about a really coarse granite as about a really fine one only by a manifold increase in the amount of money and time available for the purchase and analysis of thin sections.   To obtain point-to-point information of comparable precision will often be prohibitively expensive.   To maintain precision of group means, however, will usually involve only moderately greater cost in the coarse-grained rocks.   This should be regarded as a minimum objective.   Petrographers obliged to do modal analysis on coarse rocks will probably find it necessary to rest content with simple sample plans in which maximum interest centers on group means.

11

The Holmes effect and
the lower limit of coarseness
in modal analysis

1. THE TWO LIMITS OF COARSENESS IN MODAL ANALYSIS

In the last three chapters we have been concerned with the upper limit of coarseness in modal analysis. Other things being equal, the efficiency of the measurement area as a sample of the hand specimen decreases, i.e., what we have defined as analytical error *increases*, as the number of grain sections it contains decreases. In theory, modal analysis never becomes impossible because of this decrease; it simply becomes increasingly unprofitable. Now the size of analytical error that can be tolerated will vary with experimental design and objective; similarly, the coarseness at which this limit is reached will vary from rock to rock and, as we have seen, is itself a matter for experimental determination. Except for our insistence on its purely practical nature, there is of course nothing novel in this formulation of the problem.

It is perhaps not so commonly realized that there is also a *lower* limit of coarseness, a *fineness* beneath which the method should not be used. This lower limit involves something more fundamental than mere loss of efficiency. The source of the difficulty is a systematic error, or bias, arising from the fact that when grain diameters and cross-sectional areas become sufficiently small it is no longer possible to confine the observations to a single *surface* or area. In some cases, including the one we shall presently discuss in detail, apparent efficiency, as judged by experimental scatter, may remain very high long after the grains have become so small that the results of the analysis bear no close relation to the actual composition of the measurement area.

When individual grains are small enough the microscopist automatically tends to "look into" the thin section rather than merely at it, and may find that he cannot locate, with sufficient precision, the intersections of grain contacts with the surface of the thin section. It cannot be too strongly stressed that a modal analysis is an *areal* analysis. We study thin sections of finite thickness in transmitted light solely as an aid to identification. Unless we can regard our measurements as areal proportions the argument of chapter 1 fails, and there is no a priori way of demonstrating the consistence of the procedure. At the risk of being tedious, we may remind the reader that in this connection consistence means much more than concordance of results; rather it connotes a procedure, repetition of which generates a result whose mean value converges, in a probability sense, on the *true* areal composition of the measurement area. Without at least this assurance about the result of thin-section analysis we have no a priori reason to expect different analysts to agree with each other and, what is more puzzling, no apparent reason to prefer the work of those who do to that of those who do not.

Comparing the two limits of coarseness, we may say that the upper limit is controlled by the ratio of grain-section area to measurement area and the lower by the ratio of grain diameter (or radius) to thin-section thickness. When the first ratio becomes large enough the method becomes grossly inefficient and hence impractical; when the second becomes small enough the method becomes inappropriate because the results may contain serious systematic biases difficult to evaluate, or even to detect, by purely experimental procedures.

2. The Lower Limit of Coarseness for Opaque Spheres in a Transparent Medium

A direct geometrical evaluation of this second limit is possible for opaque grains, of some specified shape, set in a transparent matrix. A. Holmes long ago pointed out that the amount of opaque material would be systematically overestimated by areal measurements made in transmitted light. The apparent area of any opaque grain or aggregate will always be that of its maximum cross section in the slide, whereas the measurement should be of its "true area," i.e., its area at the surface of the thin section. Thus the relative area of opaque matter on the measurement surface will generally be overestimated.

For particle shapes of low symmetry the size of the Holmes bias is rather troublesome to calculate. This is true also for highly symmetrical shapes oriented in such a way that the symmetry cannot be utilized. For spherical particles, however, the calculation is straightforward, if somewhat tedious. It is worth carrying through as an indication of the general order of magnitude of the effect for particle shapes of lower symmetry.

A sphere of radius greater than the thickness of the thin section ($r > k$) is shown in Fig. 14; the observer is situated somewhere along the positive region and the light source along the negative region of the Y-axis. The distance of the measurement surface (the upper surface of the thin section) from the base of the sphere is given by y, and an opaque area will appear in the field of vision whenever $0 < y < (2r + k)$. For $y < r$ the apparent opaque area will be identical with the true one.   In the

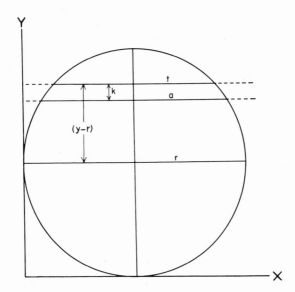

Fig. 14. Opaque sphere of radius r cut by thin section of thickness k. The light source is situated below the sphere (i.e., at some negative value of Y), and the observer is above the sphere. The radius of the true circular section on the measurement area is t, the radius of the apparent circular section is a.

region $r < y < (r + k)$ the apparent area will be constant and equal to the area of the equatorial plane, and the true area, the one the observer should be measuring, decreases steadily as $y \to (r + k)$.   In the region $(r + k) < y < 2r$ both the true and the apparent areas decrease steadily as $y \to 2r$, but they do so at different rates and the apparent area is always larger than the true.   Finally, in the region $2r < y < (2r + k)$, the true area is zero—the sphere does not intersect the measurement surface of the thin section—but the apparent area persists until $y = (2r + k)$, at which point it vanishes.   Thus at any y value in the region $0 < y < (2r + k)$ the apparent area is never less than the true, and in the region $r < y < (2r + k)$ it is always larger.   Estimates of the area of the circular section will inevitably be subject to a positive bias if made in transmitted light, and our problem is to estimate the size of this bias. In order to do so we first find the expected or average values for the true and apparent opaque areas.   The bias is simply the difference between the two.

Our interest is only with those sections in which the apparent area is greater than zero; this will be true of all sections in the region $0 < y < (2r + k)$ and only of such sections.   We therefore specify that elevations of measurement areas above the base of the sphere are to be chosen simply at random, so that the probability that some particular elevation, y, is equal to or less than any arbitrary value, h, is simply

$$Pr\{0 < y \leqslant h\} = \frac{h}{2r + k} \qquad 0 < h < (2r + k)$$

The cumulative frequency is accordingly

$$F(h) = \frac{1}{2r + k} \int_0^h dy \qquad (11.1)$$

which is clearly equal to unity when $h = (2r + k)$.

Now the area (A_t) of any particular circular section at the measurement surface will be

$$\left. \begin{array}{ll} A_t = \pi[r^2 - (r - y)^2] \text{ in the region } 0 < y < r \\[2mm] A_t = \pi[r^2 - (y - r)^2] \text{ in the region } r < y < 2r \\[2mm] \text{and} \quad A_t = 0 \qquad\qquad \text{in the region } 2r < y < (2r + k) \end{array} \right\} \quad (11.2)$$

But $r^2 - (r - y)^2 = r^2 - (y - r)^2 = 2ry - y^2$, and we may combine the first two lines of eq. (11.2) as

$$A_t = \pi(2ry - y^2) \text{ in the region } 0 < y < 2r \qquad (11.2a)$$

From eqs. (11.1) and (11.2a) we have at once that the expected value or long-range average for the true area is

$$E(A_t) = \frac{\pi}{2r + k} \int_0^{2r} (2ry - y^2)\, dy = \frac{4\pi r^3}{3(2r + k)} \qquad (11.3)$$

For the apparent area, (A_a), the situation is a little more complicated. Below the equatorial plane it is identical with the true area, e.g.,

$$A_a = \pi(2ry - y^2) \text{ in the region } 0 < y < r \qquad (11.4a)$$

It is equal to the area of the equatorial plane if $r < y < (r + k)$, or

$$A_a = \pi r^2 \qquad \text{in the region } r < y < (r + k) \qquad (11.4b)$$

Finally, for $y > (r + k)$, we have

$$A_a = \pi[r^2 - (y - r - k)^2] = \pi[2r(y - k) - (y - k)^2] \quad (11.4c)$$

From eqs. (11.1) and (11.4) we have, for the expected value of the apparent area,

$$E(A_a) = \frac{\pi}{2r + k} \int_0^r (2ry - y^2)\, dy + \frac{\pi r^2}{2r + k} \int_r^{r+k} dy$$

$$+ \frac{\pi}{2r + k} \int_{r+k}^{2r+k} [2r(y - k) - (y - k)^2]\, dy$$

$$= \frac{4\pi r^3}{3(2r + k)} + \frac{\pi r^2 k}{2r + k} \quad (11.5)$$

The bias, or expected excess of apparent area over true, obtained by subtracting eq. (11.3) from eq. (11.5), is

$$B = E(A_a) - E(A_t) = \frac{\pi r^2 k}{2r + k} \quad (11.6)$$

The apparent area will be $\dfrac{E(A_a)}{E(A_t)}$ times the true one, so that in the rather special case in which a correction would be justified the proper procedure would be to multiply the observed value by

$$C = \frac{E(A_t)}{E(A_a)} = \frac{4r}{4r + 3k} \quad (11.7)$$

Although the figure illustrates only the circumstance in which $r > k$, the reader can easily satisfy himself that the proof holds also for $r < k$. The region $0 < y < (2r + k)$ contains only (and all) sections in which $A_a > 0$ whether $r > k$ or $r < k$; eq. (11.1) thus holds in either case. Similarly, eqs. (11.2) and (11.4) define the areas of sections through the spherical particle whether $r > k$ or $r < k$. Hence eqs. (11.3) and (11.5) also hold in either case. We are thus in a position to calculate the appropriate correction factor C for any ratio of spherical radius to thin-section thickness. Table 11.1 shows C for selected values of r/k in the range $200 \geqslant (r/k) \geqslant 0.033$. The second column of the table shows r in millimeters for $k = 0.03$ mm., the standard thickness used in most petrographic laboratories. The third column of the table, of course, applies strictly only to opaque spherical particles in a transparent matrix, but it gives a good idea of the general nature of the effect for particles of less symmetrical shape.

TABLE 11.1. CORRECTION FACTORS FOR CROSS-SECTION AREAS OF
OPAQUE SPHERES IN A TRANSPARENT MATRIX, MEASURED IN
TRANSMITTED LIGHT

Ratio of Spherical Radius (r) to Section Thickness (k)	Spherical Radius for Standard Thickness ($k = 0.03$ mm.)	"Correction" Factor $\left(C = \dfrac{4r}{4r + 3k} \right)$
200	6.0	0.9963
100	3.0	0.9926
50	1.5	0.9852
33	1.0	0.9780
20	0.6	0.9639
10	0·3	0.9302
5	0.15	0.8696
4	0.12	0.8421
3	0.09	0.8002
2	0.06	0.7273
1	0.03	0.5714
0.50	0.015	0.4000
0.33	0.010	0.3077
0.25	0.0075	0.2500
0.20	0.0060	0.2105
0.10	0.0030	0.1176
0.067	0.0020	0.0816
0.033	0.0010	0.0426

3. THE POSSIBLE PRACTICAL IMPORTANCE OF THE LOWER LIMIT OF COARSENESS

The importance attached to the table will vary with the interests of the reader. In many plutonic rocks, for instance, opaque constituents are present only in accessory amounts, if at all, and analytical results are recorded to tenths of a per cent. On the assumption that the opaque particles are truly spherical, an analysis reporting 0.1 per cent of opaque accessories, for instance, would not be high by a reportable amount unless the (spherical) radius of the opaque granules were less than 0.02 mm. in a slide of 0.03-mm. thickness. Similarly, an analytical result of 0.5 per cent opaque accessories would not be high by a reportable amount unless the spherical radius of the opaque particles were less than 0.2 mm. At 1 per cent the critical spherical radius is 0.4 mm. In work of this sort the Holmes effect is not the likely to be of much importance.

If the amount of opaque material is large or the opaque particles are exceedingly small, however, the situation is very different. Estimates of magnetite dust in plagioclase, for instance, could easily be absurdly high.

If the radius were 0.015 mm., a value not unreasonably small, the amount of dust would be overestimated by a factor of 2.5.   For a radius of 0.01 mm. the "observed" amount would be high by a factor of 3.25, and for a radius of 0.003 mm., one-tenth the thickness of the slide, the true opaque area would be a little less than one-eighth of the apparent area.

Similar difficulties may be anticipated in the analysis of fine-grained sediments, such as black shales, which contain considerable amounts of finely divided organic or other opaque material.   Under such circumstances microscopic analyses may be internally consistent—and hence useful for many geological purposes—provided specimens being compared with each other do not differ materially in grain size.   It is not to be expected, however, that the results will tell much about the modal compositions of the parent materials.   In general, they will overestimate the amount of opaque material; even a good guess as to the size of the overestimate, however, will require more information than is ordinarily available.

Elliott has argued that a bias similar to the Holmes effect may be generated by the juxtaposition of transparent minerals differing greatly in refractive index.   Although relief is strictly a property of the contacts between grains, we do generally identify it with the mineral whose index differs more from that of the mounting medium.   Accordingly, if we are unable to locate the intersections of grain contacts with some specific measurement plane—usually the upper surface of the thin section—our measurements may well be subject to the Holmes effect even though all the constituents involved are transparent.

Even when index difference is not enough to produce strong relief, inability to locate the measurement surface may introduce large constant errors.   Most of the members of a swarm of perthitic albite blebs, for instance, may be below the surface of the thin section, yet all may show the appropriate Becke line against the host, and differences in birefringence or extinction will not be obscured by the fact that many of the blebs are partly or entirely beneath the measurement surface.

If there is no tendency for some particular transparent mineral to mantle the opaque granules, the Holmes effect could be overcome by measuring the amount of opaque material in reflected rather than transmitted light.   This procedure would always eliminate the bias as far as the opaques are concerned, but if some one of the transparent minerals systematically mantled the opaque particles, the amount of this material relative to other transparent minerals would be underestimated in transmitted light.

The general case, in which neither mineral is opaque, is both far more common and considerably more difficult to assess.   There is need of a good experimental study of the problem, and without such a study we are not likely to know just how serious it is. The difficulty arises because the analyst either does not or cannot confine his observations to the surface of the thin section. If the failure is merely a matter of preference, the remedy is obvious. If, however, the rock is so fine-grained that individual particles are of the order of magnitude of imperfections in the surface (or depth of focus of the microscope), the lower limit of modal analysis has been reached. Even if we knew the appropriate corrections in the latter case, they would probably be so large that most of us would hesitate to use them.

It may be useful to point out in closing that what is involved is not grain size in any absolute sense. Rather, it is the *ratio of grain size to thin-section thickness* that governs the size of the bias. It may be calculated from Table 11.1, for instance, that particles of spherical radius 0.06 mm. will be subject to a 37.5 per cent overestimate in thin sections of standard thickness. If however, the thickness of the thin section could be reduced by a factor of 3, the overestimate would be reduced to something less than 15 per cent. If it were possible to prepare slides one-fifth the standard thickness, it would be only 7.5 per cent.

Appendix 1

_____Statistical references

Statistics has undergone a remarkable development since the First World War, and since World War II there has been a proliferation of excellent textbooks on the subject. Although the level of mathematical maturity expected of the reader seems to be steadily rising, it is still possible to get a good intuitive grasp of the more practical aspects of the subject without much first-hand knowledge of the mathematical derivations. This requires careful and close study of one of the textbooks, such as Snedecor or Dixon and Massey, in which extensive, well-planned arithmetic calculation and argumentation substitute for mathematics. A man trained, or self-trained, in this fashion is ready to cooperate effectively with professional statisticians familiar with his subject-matter specialty and often even employed to help him in the design of his experiments.

Unfortunately, this is not the situation in which most geologists find themselves. Our problem is to create an intellectual environment which may one day lead to the type of collaboration now taken as a matter of course in agronomy, animal husbandry, or industrial control. Most of us have to assume that we shall only rarely be able to consult directly with statisticians and that, when we are able to do so, the statistical expert involved will usually have very little knowledge of and practically no interest in geology. We cannot expect him to be able to detect or correct loose thinking and inadequate planning with anything like the skill and proficiency that characterize his activity in more familiar fields.

In short we have to do most of our work for ourselves, and we cannot suppose that experimental designs developed in other fields will necessarily be directly applicable in ours. Under the circumstances it seems to me that the attitude fostered by an appreciation of fundamentals, however incomplete, is likely to be more useful than either facility in calculation or familiarity with the jargon that has grown up about experimental design. In the citations that follow, therefore, the primary reference is to an elementary treatise of the type intended to introduce the reader to the mathematical aspects of the subject. The book by H. Cramér, _The Elements of Probability Theory and Some of Its Applications_ (Wiley, 1955), contains at least some discussion of almost every topic required. Usually there are additional references to one or more of the following:

Anderson, R. L., and G. A. Bancroft (1952). _Statistical Theory in Research._ New York, McGraw-Hill Book Co.

Cochran, W. G. (1953). _Sampling Techniques._ New York, John Wiley & Sons.

Mood, A. McF. (1950). *Introduction to the Theory of Statistics.* New York, McGraw-Hill Book Co.

Snedecor, G. W. (1946). *Statistical Methods,* 4th ed. Ames, Ia., Iowa State College Press.

Wilks, S. S. (1952). *Elementary Statistical Analysis.* Princeton, N.J., Princeton University Press.

Citation to all these is by authors' names. It has been desirable at times, and necessary once, to refer to the journal literature.

CHAPTER 1. THE GEOMETRICAL BASIS OF MODAL ANALYSIS

Calculation of expected values: Cramér, chapter 5, pp. 57–89. See also Wilks, chapter 4, pp. 58–97, especially pp. 95–96.

Consistence and bias: Cramér, pp. 191–194; Mood, pp. 148–150; Anderson and Bancroft, p. 93.

Central limits theorem: Cramér, pp. 114–116; Mood, pp. 136–139.

Random numbers: Cramér, p. 256. See also Snedecor, pp. 9–14, which contains Tippett's Table of Random Numbers and instructions on how to use it. A larger table is given in Interstate Commerce Commission Table of 105,000 Random Decimal Digits, Statement No. 4914, File 261-A-1, 1949.

Sampling, simple-random, stratified-random, and systematic: Snedecor, pp. 1–2. For an excellent general discussion of sampling see W. G. Cochran, F. Mosteller, and J. W. Tukey, Principles of sampling, *J. Am. Stat. Assoc.,* vol. 49, pp. 13–35, 1954.

CHAPTER 2. THE MODAL ANALYSIS OF BANDED ROCKS

This chapter is mostly plane geometry and trigonometry. The standard deviation mentioned in the discussion of Fig. 8 is for a uniform or rectangular distribution, of range $-1.5 \leqslant x \leqslant 1.5$. (The *mean* of such a distribution is obviously 0; hence the banding introduces no systematic error.) For the calculation of the *second moment of a rectangular distribution* see Cramér, pp. 74–75 and example 2 of p. 75. The standard deviation is the square root of the second moment about the mean.

For sampling, see references for chapter 1.

CHAPTER 4. THE REPRODUCIBILITY OF THIN-SECTION ANALYSES, I

The model for the counting error is taken as the *binomial distribution,* for the calculation of the *mean* and *variance* of which see Cramér, p. 90.

Error of a mean based on n observations: Cramér, p. 79.

Error of a difference: This is a special case of the *addition rule for standard deviations,* for which see Cramér, pp. 77–79, but is not treated explicitly in any of the textbooks used here. In older works it often served as the starting point for discussions of errors of observation; the use of duplicates in a practical example is well described by Snedecor, pp. 72–73, where the properties of random paired differences are stated without proof (p. 73).

CHAPTER 5. THE REPRODUCIBILITY OF THIN-SECTION ANALYSES, II

Variance analysis: Cramér, pp. 246–253. See also Snedecor, chapters 10 and 11, which seems to the writer to be the best introduction to the subject for the non-mathematical reader. The arrangement of the MIT test is of the type called "randomized blocks," discussed by Snedecor at the beginning of chapter 11 (pp. 253–255). The reader who has had no previous introduction to the subject should certainly study Snedecor's chapter 10 carefully before beginning chapter 11.

Estimation of individual analyst variances from paired differences: The procedure followed in the last half of chapter 5 is almost certainly not new, but the author has found no published reference to it. The general approach was suggested by J. M. Cameron.

CHAPTER 6. IDENTIFICATION AND TABULATION CONVENTIONS

Effect of heterogeneity of subgroup variances: see W. G. Cochran. Some consequences when the assumptions for the analysis of variance are not satisfied, *Biometrics*, vol. 3, pp. 22–38, 1947, especially pp. 28–32.

CHAPTER 8. EFFECT OF GRAIN SIZE AND AREA OF MEASUREMENT ON ANALYTICAL ERROR

Confidence intervals about the sample standard deviation: Cramér, pp. 203–204.

Regression analysis and least-squares fitting of a straight line: Cramér, pp. 133–136; Wilks, pp. 236–273; Snedecor, pp. 103–137.

CHAPTER 9. A MEASURE OF COARSENESS IN THE GRANITIC FABRIC

Variance analysis: see references for chapter 5 above.

Regression analysis: see references for chapter 8 above.

CHAPTER 10. THE CONTROL OF ANALYTICAL ERROR BY REPLICATION

Construction of the replication schedules shown in Figs. 11–13 is based entirely on the definition of *the standard error*, or *error of the mean*, for which see Cramér, p. 79.

Concerning *relative precision of systematic and random sampling:* see Cochran, pp. 162–164.

The latter part of the chapter is essentially an adaptation of some of the procedure suggested by Cameron, 1951. The use of components of variance in preparing schedules for sampling of baled wool, *Biometrics*, vol. 7, pp. 83–96, 1951.

CHAPTER 11. THE HOLMES EFFECT AND THE LOWER LIMIT OF COARSENESS IN MODAL ANALYSIS

Calculation of expected values: see references for chapter 1.

Consistence and bias: see references for chapter 1.

Appendix 2

A simple method of calculating z_____

In chapter 2 the geometrical construction by which the excess is isolated always locates it in the proper band type within the original measurement area. This is useful for graphical purposes, and for ω values at which the origin and one other corner of the measurement area lie on band contacts, the so-called "integral intersections," the calculation of z is not excessively tedious.

An indirect procedure, however, is much easier, particularly for intermediate values of ω. This consists in *enlarging* the measurement area so that it conforms to rule b or c. The added portion will then contain an excess exactly equal in size and opposite in sign to that of the original. If l and w are integral multiples of the band width t, and either one is greater than an odd but less than an even multiple of the projected band width, the area of the excess will then always be given by an equation of the form

$$e = \left(\left|\frac{k_1}{\sin \omega} - w\right|\right)\left(\left|\frac{k_2}{\cos \omega} - l\right|\right)$$

where $k_1 \leqslant w$, $k_2 \leqslant l$, and both k_1 and k_2 are integers.

The procedure of "completing" the measurement area is shown in Fig. $A1$, in which $w = 3$, $l = 5$, and $\omega = 30°$. The original measurement area $OMNS$ has no integral intersections. It is enlarged to $OMPR$, and, since OR is an even integral multiple of the projected band width, the enlarged figure satisfies rule b. Since $OMNS$ contains an excess of one band over the other and $OMPR$ does not, the added strip $SNPR$ must contain an excess exactly equal to that in $OMNS$ but opposite in sign. By construction, the triangular area V is equal to the triangular area V', so that the excess in the added strip is simply the stippled area $NPQT$.

But $NP = SR = \left(\dfrac{2}{\sin \omega} - 3\right)$, $QP = T'M = \left(5 - \dfrac{4}{\cos \omega}\right)$, and the excess is, accordingly

$$e = (NP)(QP) = \left(\frac{2}{\sin \omega} - 3\right)\left(5 - \frac{4}{\cos \omega}\right).$$

It lies in a band of type B, so the original measurement area must contain a similar excess of band type A. For the original area, therefore,

$$100z = 3.33 \left(\frac{2}{\sin \omega} - 3\right)\left(5 - \frac{4}{\cos \omega}\right) = 1.252.$$

106

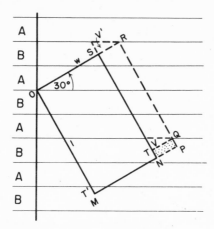

Fig. $A1$. Locating the excess by "completing" the measurement area. The added area $SNPR$ contains an excess of band type B, shown by the stippled area $TNPQ$. The original area $OMNS$ accordingly contains an identical excess of band type A.

Similar calculations for the critical region of Fig. 8 yield the results given in Table $A1$.

TABLE $A1$. $100z$ FOR $28° < \omega < 49°$

ω	$100z$	ω	$100z$	ω	$100z$
28.11^a	1.845	36.00	0.076	42.00	−0.014
29.00	1.599	36.87^a	No excess	43.00	−0.105
30.00	1.252	37.00	−0.009	44.00	−0.226
31.00	0.981	38.00	−0.063	45.00	−0.375
32.00	0.730	39.00^a	No excess	46.00	−0.555
33.00	0.516	40.00	0.082	47.00	−0.764
34.00	0.336	41.00	0.048	48.00	−1.005
35.00	0.190	41.81^a	No excess	49.00	−1.278
				49.17^a	−1.328

^{a} Integral intersections shown by points in Fig. 8.

References

Bankier, J. D. (1955). The theory of thin-section analysis: A discussion, *J. Geol.*, vol. 63, pp. 287–288.

Barringer, A. R. (1953). The preparation of polished sections of ores, etc., *Trans. Inst. Min. Met.*, vol. 63, pp. 21–41.

Cameron, J. M. (1951). The use of components of variance in preparing schedules for sampling baled wool, *Biometrics*, vol. 7, pp. 83–96.

Chayes, F. (1949). A simple point counter for thin-section analysis, *Am. Min.*, vol. 34, pp. 1–11.

Chayes, F. (1955). A point counter based on the Leitz mechanical stage, *Am. Min.*, vol. 40, pp. 126–127.

Chayes, F., and H. W. Fairbairn (1951). A test of the precision of thin-section analysis by point counter, *Am. Min.*, vol. 36, pp. 704–712.

Cochran, W. G. (1953). *Sampling Techniques*, New York, John Wiley & Sons.

Delesse, A. (1848). Procédé méchanique pour déterminer la composition des roches, *Ann. mines*, vol. 13, pp. 379–388.

Dollar, A. T. J. (1937). An integrating micrometer for the geometrical analysis of rocks, *Min. Mag.*, vol. 24, pp. 577–594.

Elliott, R. B. (1952). The superposition error in the micrometric analysis of rocks, *Min. Mag.*, vol. 29, pp. 833–837.

Fairbairn, H. W., et al. (1951). A cooperative investigation of precision and accuracy in chemical, spectrochemical and modal analysis of silicate rocks, U.S. Geol. Survey Bull. 980 (see especially part 5, pp. 59–68).

Ford, I. H. (1954). A microscope stage and integrating point counter for micrometric analysis of rocks, *J. Sci. Instr.*, vol. 31, pp. 164–165.

Glagolev, A. A. (1933). On the geometrical methods of quantitative mineralogic analysis of rocks, *Trans. Inst. Econ. Min., Moscow*, vol. 59.

Glagolev, A. A. (1934). Quantitative analysis with the microscope . . . by the point method, *Eng. Min. J.*, vol. 135, p. 399.

Griffiths, J. G., and M. A. Rosenfeld (1954). Operator variation in experimental research, *J. Geol.*, vol. 62, pp. 74–91.

Holmes, A. H. (1927). *Petrographic Methods and Calculations*, London, Murby and Co. (see p. 317).

Hunt, W. F. (1924). An improved Wentworth recording micrometer, *Am. Min.*, vol. 9, pp. 190–193.

Hurlbut, C. (1939). An electric counter for thin-section analysis, *Am. J. Sci.*, vol. 237, pp. 253–261.

Johannsen, A. (1919). A planimeter method for the determination of the percentage composition of rocks, *J. Geol.*, vol. 27, pp. 276-285.

Joly, J. (1903). The petrological examination of paving sets, *Proc. Roy. Dublin Soc.*, vol. 10, pp. 62–92 (see especially pp. 83–84).

Julien, A. A. (1902). Genesis of the amphibole schists and serpentines of Manhattan Island, N. Y., *Bull. Geol. Soc. Amer.*, vol. 14, pp. 460–468.

Larsen, E. S., and F. S. Miller (1935). The Rosiwal method and the modal determination of rocks, *Am. Min.*, vol. 20, pp. 260–273.

Lincoln, F., and H. L. Rietz (1913). The determination of the relative volume of the components of rocks by mensuration methods, *Econ. Geol.*, vol. 8, pp. 120–139.

Richardson, W. A. (1923). A micrometric study of the St. Austell granite. *Quart. J. Geol. Soc., London*, vol. 79, pp. 546–576.

Rosenfeld, M. (1954). A modification of the Chayes point counter stage, *Am. Min.*, vol. 39, pp. 834–836.

Rosiwal, A. (1898). Ueber geometrische Gesteinsanalysen usw., *Verh. der k. k. Geolog. Reichsanstalt Wien*, pp. 143–175.

Shand, S. J. (1916). A recording micrometer for rock analysis, *J. Geol.*, vol. 24, pp. 394–403.

Sollas, W. J. (1889). Contributions to a knowledge of the granites of Leinster, *Trans. Roy. Irish Acad., Dublin*, vol. 29, pp. 427–512 (see especially pp. 471–472).

Sorby, H. C. (1856). On slaty cleavage as exhibited in the Devonian limestones of Devonshire, *Phil. Mag.*, vol. 11, pp. 20–37.

Wentworth, C. J. (1923). An improved recording micrometer for rock analysis, *J. Geol.*, vol. 31, pp. 228–232.

Index